WALKING
TOWARDS
THUNDER

ŕ
Se

For all the advocates and survivors of childhood sexual abuse, and those who didn't survive.

'There comes a time when one must take a position that is neither safe, nor popular, but he must take it because conscience tells him it is right.'
– Martin Luther King Jnr

CONTENTS

PROLOGUE

When a person speaks out from within an institution against that institution, they know reprisals are coming. Institutions carry it in their DNA, in-built self-protection, if you like. When working as a police detective, a priest who assisted me in a clergy child sexual abuse case was shunned and effectively exiled by fellow clergy. Gillian Snedden, who assisted police to investigate her politician boss, Milton Orkopoulos, for sexually abusing children, was bullied and harassed before losing her job. As did Dr Lynn Simpson, a vet who spoke out after a report concerning horrendous conditions and suffering of animals in Australia's live-export industry written by her was inexplicably leaked within the industry by person/s unknown. I have heard similar stories from police, health workers, private industry professionals and university staff. No one institution has a monopoly on reprisal; they all practise it to punish and deter.

Ostracism is the most effective weapon used to silence whistleblowers. Of course, those at the top don't get involved. They don't need to. I have seen it within the NSW Police Force all too often. Deborah Locke, Ken Jurotte, Lucie Litchfield are but a few of its victims. Of course, there are police rules to say it shouldn't happen. Policies are waved about, with units set up to protect internal witnesses. They are great public-relations exercises, but my experience with them was little beyond glossy pamphlets and welfare calls. No real effort was made to stop the victimisation. Senior police talked the talk while holding up, to my mind, their hollow guidelines. A facade to comply with legislation, government policies and public expectation.

Before other events overtook my life, I toyed with the idea of writing a memoir about my police career. I wanted to write about growing up in a western Sydney housing commission estate. About a houso kid wanting to be a cop, who made that happen but then found out what the NSW Police Force was really like in the 1970s and 80s era of corrupt cops like Roger Rogerson.

It wasn't all going to be serious. I had stories that had always got laughs at backyard barbecues and in police station meal rooms. I never intended it for sale, just a hobby – that is, if I ever got around to writing it.

When the NSW Special Commission of Inquiry, the Cunneen Inquiry, got underway, lawyers for the NSW Police Force attacked me over my musings to one day write a book. It was portrayed as something sinister, my motives suspect and self-serving. One officer suggested I had spoken out on child abuse purely to sell a book. Another inferred I was an author who had already written a novel. Neither accusation was true, but the truth wasn't going to get in the way of these detractors. To my astonishment, questioning during the Cunneen Inquiry over this issue was allowed to be raised time and again, day after day. I received summonses demanding I hand over any material I had written on clergy child sexual abuse. I didn't produce anything, because there was nothing to produce. Still not satisfied, they recalled me to the Cunneen Inquiry months after the scheduled hearings had concluded. Demands for anything I had written were renewed. Exasperated, I offered my computer hard drive or anything else they wanted for forensic checking. I simply could not produce what did not exist. Nevertheless, an accusing finger continued to be pointed. Suggesting I put myself and those I loved through hell just to write a book was, to me, laughable. I had only ever sought to tell the truth about the Church cover-up and bring those responsible to justice. It was that simple. But for some, the truth wasn't palatable. Factions within the NSW Police Force were uncomfortable with a senior officer speaking out, even though the Child Abuse Royal Commission would eventually confirm that everything I said was right. They needed another motive, and my writing a book seemed the best they could come up with. After all this nonsense I vowed never to write a book. I didn't want anyone cynically saying, *I told you so.*

•

In late 2013 when I believed my giving evidence to the Cunneen Inquiry had concluded, my wife, Penny, and I stayed in the home of Chrissie and Anthony Foster, whose daughters were victims of clergy child sexual abuse. What concerned Anthony were matters the Inquiry didn't examine, the bits redacted, suppressed or omitted. Like me, he couldn't understand why the truth, the whole truth, was not part of its scope. The Fosters had endured similar battles against the Church when they tried to expose the history of the priest who abused their daughters.

When Anthony said, 'You should write a book and say what really happened,' I laughed, telling him it wasn't an option.

'Why?' he inquired. Anthony listened to my reasons before saying: 'Peter, if you don't write a book, you'll be playing into their hands. That's why they raised it. They're frightened that one day you will write the truth, the whole truth.'

I put what Anthony said to one side. The Child Abuse Royal Commission was beginning and, at that time, I had simply had enough. I just wanted to put it behind me.

As the Child Abuse Royal Commission got underway, I was contacted by several publishers. At speaking engagements strangers urged me to write, suspecting there was more to my story. They were right, but I elected to say nothing.

In 2014 I received the Cunneen Inquiry's preliminary findings. To say I was outraged would be an understatement. In my view, the limited scope of its terms of reference necessarily meant that it would inevitably gloss over or ignore significant issues. I knew some criticism of me was coming, I expected no less. I don't pretend to be perfect and was prepared to put my hand up for any mistakes I had made. Even so, the Cunneen Inquiry's final report tore me to shreds as an unreliable and discredited witness. I felt sick. I considered saying something publicly, but felt that anything I offered would be judged in the context of the official report. I accepted the discrediting as the price I had to pay.

It wasn't easy, but I put the Cunneen Inquiry behind me. My work toward a Child Abuse Royal Commission had succeeded. I consoled myself in having lost a battle but won a war.

My 2015 retirement dinner from the NSW Police Force was attended by former colleagues and people I had helped during my career, Chrissie and Anthony included. At night's end, Chrissie handed me a gift-wrapped box. Opening it, I found a pen.

'Start writing', she said. Since then I have done some detective work of my own. What I discovered shocked me. It not only went to the heart of the Church, but the police force, government and judicial process.

I had been through a lot, and not just in terms of investigating child sexual abuse. The vast majority of my 36-year career was spent on the front line, where I was exposed to more horrors than most. My treatment by the NSW Police Force exacerbated that, and I was diagnosed with Post Traumatic Stress Disorder (PTSD). After years of counselling, I was referred to a psychiatrist and together we worked through the issues surrounding the Cunneen Inquiry and my treatment by senior police. My psychiatrist understood. His clients were mostly emergency services personnel, police officers and war veterans. Failure at senior levels of institutions, he told me, was a common theme. He handed me a book one of his clients wrote about the Vietnam War. It told of Australian soldiers, mates, killed in battle after what he described as failures at senior level. Those senior officers were never held to account, and the author never got over it. He had written the book as much for his own healing as to reveal the truth. I started to think that there might be something to this. Some months later, I started to write. My words were disjointed at first, but eventually I saw that it could be put together, and I could tell my story. Although for legal reasons some of what I would like to have said has been omitted.

I know that what I have written here is going to be judged by others, and that prospect is daunting. The quotes I cite about child abuse perpetrators and the cover up of their crimes, particularly accounts from former clergy and sexual abuse survivors, I obtained from proved sources, albeit after the fact. The horrors recounted will shock but I hope also remind us all to keep the focus on the protection of our children. The Catholic Church consists of congregations of many good laypersons and priests said to make up the 'Church'. Throughout my story I have used the word Church extensively. I want to clarify from the start that my use of the word refers to the Catholic Church hierarchy.

Some will say I am singling out the Catholic Church when other religious institutions were also complicit in crimes against children and the concealment of those crimes. It is true the Catholic Church was not the only offender, although the Child Abuse Royal Commission did establish it was by far the worst perpetrator of all religious institutions. It features in my story not for that reason, but because it was at the centre of what I investigated as a police detective.

It has also been a struggle with my PTSD. I don't profess to have literary ability – after so many years it has been hard to learn to not write in police jargon. Instead of saying a male alighted from the vehicle and decamped in a northerly direction, I have tried to explain a man got out of a car and ran towards some shops – so, forgive me if it doesn't flow like a Stephen King or Danielle Steel. I'm just an ex-cop telling his story in the hope that it will make a difference in the protection of our children and the way we treat those who speak out when wrongs are being committed by those with all the power.

Please note that this book discusses traumatic events, abuse and suicide. If you or someone you know is thinking about suicide, you can call Lifeline on 13 11 14, Kids Helpline on 1800 551 800, Mensline Australia on 1300 789 978 or the Suicide Call Back Service 1300 659 467.

CHAPTER 1

STEPPING UP

I hadn't been to work for months. I still loved being a cop, but I was worn down by internal issues and PTSD. I was still a police officer, but as time passed the prospect of returning to work looked less and less likely.

By September 2012 my wife, Penny, was taking a well-deserved break. Penny had travelled the ups and downs of my career over more than thirty years. She too knew all the heartbreak, anger, frustration, stress and fear. In some respects she had done it tougher than me, suffering a breakdown following threats made when I undertook a difficult internal investigation. Friends were taking her for a weekend shopping trip to Sydney.

The morning before Penny left, I pondered what I would do while she was away. Outside was a glorious spring morning, the kind we get to enjoy in the Hunter Valley before summer cranks up the heat, turning everything a dull grey-brown. I sat looking at the dappled light playing between the leaves on the pavers below our cedar tree. A few tree roots were lifting the odd paver, and I contemplated some repairs. Penny had never wanted the tree planted there in the first place, and

I knew that if I completed the repairs while she was away I wouldn't hear the inevitable, 'I told you not to plant it there.'

Despite her misgivings, she wouldn't now do without that tree. Its broad arms shaded our wrought-iron setting where we regularly had morning tea.

As I downed the last of my breakfast, I caught the tail of something on the radio. It was just a small piece, but it pricked my ears. Journalist Joanne McCarthy and the *Newcastle Herald* had organised a meeting calling for a Royal Commission into child sexual abuse within the Catholic Church. An inquiry of that nature, I knew, was long overdue.

'I might head down to that,' I said.

Penny looked up. 'Will the lady you had to return the photos to be there?'

Pat Feenan had loaned me some photographs of her son Daniel and his abuser, Catholic priest James Patrick Fletcher, to help in the trial of Father David O'Hearn, yet another Hunter Valley priest charged with sexually abusing boys. I knew how important the photographs were, so I had kept them at home, concerned they would be lost if left behind in my office when I took sick leave. I found Pat's number and, as luck would have it, she said, 'Yes, I'll be there with some friends. It'll be nice to see you, Peter.'

So, it was arranged. I decided to knock over the paving on Saturday before heading to the Newcastle meeting the following morning. I could never have contemplated then, but it would be a decision that would alter my world, and that of so many others.

The drive to Newcastle that next morning took about an hour. As others were heading to Sunday Church services, I headed to a meeting calling for a Royal Commission into child abuse within their Churches.

The crowd was bigger than I expected. Somehow amid the throng of people pouring into the Newcastle Panthers (now the Newcastle NEX) Club auditorium I found Pat Feenan nestled between two friends. A petite woman, Pat compensated for her height with a resolute determination to seek justice for the evils perpetrated upon her family. If hell hath no fury like a woman scorned, then Pat was the right person to stand up to the Church. It wasn't unbridled anger, more an outrage restrained by reason and a resolve to see justice. I mostly saw the other Pat, the one that existed before the Church cast an evil shadow. The warm, caring mother whose eyes smiled like those of her Irish ancestors.

After years of contact surrounding Fletcher's trial, Pat and I drifted back to our worlds, until I called about the photos. There had always been a firm respect between us. She was a strong woman, a remarkable woman. Pat had been to hell and back following the shock revelation that her eldest son, her beloved Daniel, had been sexually abused as a child, raped time and again by a trusted friend, Father Jim Fletcher. Of all the horrors I had been exposed to in my career, Daniel's case is one that affected me more than I liked to admit.

The crowd continued to file in as I handed Pat an envelope with her photos. We exchanged a few words before I took a chair. Fortunately Pat had kept me a seat, otherwise I would have been standing with others along the back wall. I was surprised by the size of the audience. Staff were also taken aback as they frantically darted back and forth for ever more chairs. The high interest shouldn't have surprised me. Rape of the Hunter Valley's children by priests wasn't new. It had been going on for decades.

•

3

The arrest and charging of Father Vincent Ryan in 1995 rocked the Hunter community. Many were also shocked to learn that another priest knew of Ryan's crimes as far back as the 1970s but did nothing. As a result, more boys were raped and at least one committed suicide. When a police officer reported the Church cover-up, the Department of Public Prosecutions (DPP) declined to prosecute.

By 1999, Father John Denham had also been charged with child sex offences. Father Denis McAlinden also came under investigation, but had already fled to Britain. The Maitland–Newcastle Diocese played down these revelations, minimising the extent of what had been happening. They were isolated cases, a couple of rotten apples. But the arrests continued. As more and more victims came forward, the number of priests before Hunter courts continued to grow. On more than one occasion I asked the NSW Police Force and its Sex Crimes Squad to investigate the cover-ups, but my reports never received a response.

As victims continued to come forward local detectives were charging one priest after another, yet incredibly, senior police failed to acknowledge or investigate the bigger picture. Journalists, including Joanne McCarthy, didn't. While police hierarchy maintained there was nothing to see, the community was concerned. One paedophile priest was bad enough. Two, an ugly coincidence. After three or four, alarm bells should have been ringing. NSW Police had teams of analysts and intelligence units to identify crime trends. If house robberies or car thefts spike, or patterns emerge, police know they need to target those areas. In this instance reports were coming in, albeit belatedly, of children being raped. Serious crimes. The perpetrators weren't your normal crooks, they were priests. In the Hunter, most worked for the Maitland–Newcastle Catholic Diocese.

Evidence was emerging that the Church knew more than it was saying. Not only did it know, it had failed to report or prevent further abuse. Somehow, despite all their resources, police failed to take steps. Nothing happened. Exposing the scandal would have to be taken up by others.

When the number of priests abusing children surpassed ten, hard questions should have been asked. Individual police were doing great work arresting one priest after another, but it wasn't enough. The abuse had been occurring for decades and supposedly no one knew. The question was screaming out: how could so many paedophile priests abuse so many children, in one area and for so long, without anyone knowing?

If senior police – that is, experienced sergeants and commissioned officers from the rank of inspector up – couldn't sense something was wrong, the community sure could. A few journalists like Joanne McCarthy began shining a light on the abuse story, but most stayed clear of the sensitive topic. Soon victims and their families were ringing Joanne with more accounts of clergy abuse and Church inaction. The scale was disturbing. As Joanne continued to write, senior police simply responded, *Move along! Nothing to see here.*

Like I said, detectives were doing their part, but in respect to the cover-up, the upper echelons were letting everyone down. In some quarters of the police force, Joanne was looked upon as little more than a trouble maker. It was for this reason abuse survivors began to confide in her. She listened to their stories and gave them a voice. Many soon bypassed police. In Joanne they saw someone who would go after the bigger problem: senior clergy who perpetuated abuse through the Church's failure to act.

Joanne laid bare decades of institutional cover-ups that many suspected. Little had previously been said about this, yet when revealed by the *Newcastle Herald*, there was resentment from senior police. Not until 2012 was the first priest charged with concealing child sexual abuse, despite the law existing for decades. Father Tom Brennan died before facing a court weeks later, from cancer.

The scale of child sexual abuse emerging in the Hunter suggested that the systemic concealment of these crimes was extensive. In 2010 Joanne was given a statement and other Church documents by a clergy abuse survivor revealing senior clergy knew about the crimes committed upon her as a child, but failed to tell police.

In 2010 Joanne started pushing for police to examine the bigger problem. I knew she was right, but it was a view not shared by many of my colleagues. Two years had passed before the *Newcastle Herald* organised the meeting I now attended.

•

Looking around the auditorium, the crowd continued to grow. I thought they might get fifty, maybe a hundred people, but they kept coming. I recognised a number of faces. Some survivors of clergy sexual abuse, anxious families, many just concerned community members. I exchanged a few words with a former Catholic school principal before spotting another off-duty police officer in the crowd. We had spoken some years before. He too was troubled by police inaction surrounding the cover-ups. Scanning the crowd he caught my gaze. A police trait, I suppose. We both silently nodded before I sat back down.

As quickly as new seats arrived, they were filled. Many standing were happy to collect the chairs from club staff at the back of the auditorium, shuffling them forward to make yet another row. By now the crowd had doubled to at least two hundred, and still they arrived. Someone pointed out two nuns sitting inconspicuously among the crowd. On the stage to my left was a microphone, a table to the right and a row of seats. Photographers and camera operators positioned themselves around the room as the crowd swelled. I stood to make another count: it now exceeded three hundred. Leaning over to Pat and her friends I commented, 'I didn't expect this many.'

Pat looked around. Nodding at those still arriving and staff frantically searching for ever more chairs she said, 'I don't think anyone did.'

We smiled.

NSW Premier Barry O'Farrell had rejected calls for a Child Abuse Royal Commission, saying that 'police had it under control'.

That month Lake Macquarie politician Greg Piper took the proposal for a Child Abuse Royal Commission to the premier. Barry O'Farrell dismissed it, saying 'a Royal Commission would prejudice police investigations involving the Church'.

I scoffed. At the rate clergy were coming under investigation, the time would never be right.

Following on the premier's comment, Greens Party Senator David Shoebridge asked Police Minister Mike Gallacher if 'he or any member of the government received advice from police that a Royal Commission might prejudice police investigations or prosecutions?'

Gallacher said he had received no such advice. David Shoebridge then asked Deputy Police Commissioner Nick Kaldas if he had raised concerns with the premier.

'No.'

With the number of people filing into the auditorium it was obvious many disagreed with the premier. By the time the meeting started, the crowd exceeded four hundred. With no more seats, those still arriving had to stand along the walls.

Most realised a Child Abuse Royal Commission was the only way to address this systemic crime wave. Other nations had already uncovered widespread child sexual abuse and cover-ups within the Catholic Church. Ireland didn't hold just one inquiry, but a number, including the Ferns, Cloyne, Raphoe and Dublin inquiries, to name but a few. Each shocked the nation, which one Pope had described as 'the most Catholic country in the world'.

They exposed hundreds of clergy who abused thousands of children. Inquiries also found the Gardaí, the Irish Police, formed inappropriate relationships with the Church and failed to act on allegations. I knew if things were to change in Australia, a similar inquiry was needed here.

On stage, Joanne McCarthy talked with David Shoebridge and with a survivor of abuse by Father Jim Fletcher, Peter Gogarty. Someone who wasn't there was John Pirona. John had been abused as a student at Newcastle's St Pius X High School and had lived with the trauma for 32 years until, unable to cope, he had taken his life at the age of forty-five, just two months before this meeting. His wife, Tracey, and father, Lou, were there in his place. For Joanne McCarthy, John's death had been the catalyst for this meeting.

Barrister Andrew Morrison SC, of the Australian Lawyers Alliance, was also there. He had been a long-time advocate calling for a Child Abuse Royal Commission. Journalist Peter FitzSimons was running late, caught up on the F3 expressway from Sydney.

Joanne spoke passionately, her empathy for victims laid raw. Reading notes and letters from survivors, she choked. Many wept with her. Joanne made it clear that a message needed to be sent to politicians: nothing short of a Child Abuse Royal Commission would do. Looking around I wished the premier and police commissioner had been there to feel the emotion. Police stationed only a few kilometres down the road did not attend.

When Daniel Feenan was mentioned, I looked at Pat. I had never seen her this upset. Tears flowed. She had always been the strong one, the matriarch who held things together. Emotion overflowed as she was comforted by her friends. Her pain was tangible. I felt myself taking deep breaths, trying to supress my own emotion. Feeling awkwardly useless, all I could do was hand down a paper cup of water.

Pat's distress was still palpable as the speakers continued. I had arrested and helped convict Jim Fletcher for the crimes against Pat's son. Fletcher had died in gaol a little over a year into his sentence.

Tracey Pirona spoke of the loving husband and father she had married, the man who had recently left his note, 'Too much pain'. John's body was found five days later in his car, just north of Newcastle in my police command of Port Stephens. Tracey's story hurt. I felt it, but why weren't our politicians here to feel it too? To them John Pirona was just a name, another victim of the Church's failure to act.

Next to speak was Lou Pirona, John's father, a retired lawyer. We had previously sat on opposing sides in court, but today we were united. Lou spoke with a lawyer's logic, but with a father's love and passion. He told the audience that decisions shouldn't be left in the hands of 'people who don't have the character and the will to do the right thing'. Adding: 'We're just seeing the reality of the failure of a lot of people to look after people who should have been looked after, and that reality is devastating.'

Who was he talking about? Most knew that the cover-ups extended well beyond Cathedral walls. The whole rotten mess lay bubbling under the surface for decades. It wasn't as if the public didn't know, they just needed someone to act. Families like Lou's had been let down. His words resounded: *people who don't have the character and the will to do the right thing.* Was he talking about me? I'd done my bit, hadn't I?

John Pirona was one of many students abused by Father John Denham at St Pius X High School in Newcastle. In his book *The Priests*, James Miller made clear Denham wasn't the only paedophile priest at the school. For decades fellow clergy turned a blind eye to Denham's crimes. Fletcher also had a connection to the school, having raped one of his victims in the adjoining street, just outside the school fence. Coincidence? I didn't believe so.

I felt the emotion as my chest pounded and my head spun. I knew some didn't want more to be said. I had been silenced just like abuse survivors, told by senior police to stop investigating the alleged cover-up and cease speaking to survivors. Leaning forward, I rested my head in my hands, unable to look at the stage. Why the hell had I stayed? It was a stupid question with a simple answer. I cared. I'd been told time and again police shouldn't get close, we should remain detached. Some refer to it as de-humanisation. The problem was, I never really learned not to be human. I always cared. It's what motivated me to become a cop in the first place.

I had a lot bottled up, and I strained to keep it in. I knew the truth, or at least a good chunk of it. I realised that if I opened my mouth it would end my career, my reputation and impact my retirement. It would inflict hurt, and I might even face departmental charges for insubordination and breaching media policy and the like. Some senior police would have no compunction about metaphorically grabbing me by the throat. I'd seen it all before. I could be demoted and publicly ridiculed. Some would like that, so I sat telling myself, *Shut up, Pete. Just sit here and keep your mouth shut.*

Lou finished: 'He [John] carried it for many years. I just don't know what was going on in the dark recesses of his mind, notwithstanding the love his family had for him, and the love he had for his family.'

Like the families of other survivors I had met, the Pirona family were good people. They loved each other and those around them. A family like my own. The only difference being, my family was lucky.

I didn't realise I was rocking back and forth with my face still in my hands, my head pounding. Pat later told me she was worried. That was one for the books, the table had turned one hundred and eighty degrees. Pat saw I wasn't myself as everything ran through my head. I decided to play it safe and stay where I was. Keep my mouth closed. I owed it to my family. At least that was the excuse I gave myself. I knew I wouldn't be the first. Who could blame me? I'd been through enough for a dozen policing careers. I would stay where I was and do nothing. But something kept tapping, whispering, urging.

Lou went on: 'These men have to pay for what they have done, whether it's the vile act of what they did or having the knowledge of it and not doing anything about it.'

I knew he was right. There was a lot more to be uncovered. But it was now someone else's fight. I'd done enough.

Peter FitzSimons ran up the steps late and strode to the microphone wearing his customary red bandana. Speaking with authority and determination he banged his fist on the dais, 'This stops now! This cannot go on, and on, and on.'

He spoke with conviction, infecting the audience. Then he paraphrased that immortal quote by Edmund Burke, 'All that is necessary for the triumph of evil is that good men do nothing.'

His words sent me reeling. They really were talking about me. I knew, and I was doing nothing. My excuses suddenly vanished. There would be a price for what I was about to do, but I refused to think about it. I just wanted the evil to stop. I couldn't remain seated any longer. No more excuses.

I didn't know a camera was trained on Pat and it now swung to me. The cameraman didn't know who I was, but somehow sensed something. In the course of events his footage would later be played to screens across the country.

Pat looked at me. 'Are you all right?'

I didn't look back before replying, 'There's something I have to do. I'm going to speak.'

Concerned, Pat asked, 'Are you sure?'

I answered, 'If Daniel can walk into a police station I can walk onto that stage.'

Pat did not look convinced, but it was too late. As I squeezed between the seats my head was swimming. I stumbled past legs as I made my way along the aisle. I didn't want to think of what might happen. I knew there would be hell to pay for what I was about to do. I just blocked all the possible repercussions from my mind. Walking onto the stage the audience must have wondered who the hell I was.

I looked at Joanne. 'I want to speak.'

She seemed unsure.

I didn't realise how bad I looked until I saw the footage later. If I had a mirror I would have shared her reservations. My face full of emotion, contorted, jaw set and eyes welling.

Joanne echoed Pat, 'Are you all right? Are you sure you want to do this?'

'No, I'm not, but I'm speaking anyway.'

Joanne looked troubled as I took a seat and waited for David Shoebridge to finish.

Unsure what I was going to say, I at least realised this was a career-ending move. Some didn't want the Church investigated, I knew that. I won't say I wasn't scared, I was. I didn't fear the Church as much as police and politicians. Come what may, it was now too late. I would worry about all that later.

CHAPTER 2

A TOUGH BEGINNING

How did I find myself on stage calling for a Child Abuse Royal Commission and ending a thirty-six-year policing career? The explanation isn't as straightforward as some might think. My reasons were not entirely confined to the clergy child sexual abuse scandal. Understanding involves going on a journey back through my life and career.

My official police file recorded me at age eighteen telling the recruiting officer I had wanted to be a police officer since I was ten. A profession that might not have thrilled some of my ancestors.

Like most white Australians my heritage was shaped by immigrants, the last arriving before the 1860s. Some came voluntarily, others in chains. The latter were mostly defiant Irish Catholics from my mother's side. John Kennedy was a ringleader in the Society of United Irishmen. Arrested as a rebel he was transported to Australia for his part in planning the 1798 Vinegar Hill uprising. My heritage was also made up of more convicts and free settlers, but it was the rebellious Irish of which my mum's family were particularly proud.

My maternal grandfather, Eric Latimore, mesmerised me with tales of his life as a timber cutter in the Australian bush. A big, powerfully built man of Northern Irish and German ancestry, Eric was a Protestant man of God. He never swore and rarely missed church. Right was right and wrong was wrong. Life was black and white with little room for grey. He was an enormous influence on me and I loved him dearly.

My maternal grandmother, Kathleen Bruton, grew up in the shadow of the Great War. Her eldest brother was killed at Villers-Bretonneux and another came home with lungs destroyed by gas. Educated in Catholic convents throughout the Hunter and Manning Valleys, Kath was a gentle woman and an accomplished pianist.

Dad was a mix of Irish, English and Scot. The claim to fame of his great-grandfather, Robert Christie, was to have briefly harboured bushranger Ned Kelly. My family echoed with stories of the gold rush, a close shave with outlaw Jimmy Governor, but mostly pioneering and living off the land.

Growing up in the Blue Mountains town of Leura and then Sydney's eastern suburbs, Dad enlisted during the Second World War. After being discharged, he joined the NSW Fire Brigade. Mum's home was the small dairy and potato farming community of Comboyne, a pretty town cradled by mountains on the plateau between Wauchope and Wingham on the NSW mid-north coast. While nursing in Sydney, she and Dad met at a dance hall, oddly enough the same dance hall in which Dad's parents met more than thirty years before. Marrying in 1958, they lived for a time with Dad's parents at Randwick. I was born the following year, followed by my brother and eldest sister over the next two. To accommodate their growing family, Mum and Dad moved to a cramped first-floor apartment in Balmain. In 1963 we moved to the western Sydney suburb of

Green Valley, just outside Liverpool. Back then Dad's mother said we'd moved to the sticks. Green Valley was Australia's largest housing experiment, designed to house twenty-five thousand people in six thousand fibro and weatherboard homes. The suburb grew overnight and was still being built when we arrived. Most rented, but Dad wouldn't hear of it. He wanted the Australian dream of owning his own home. With a war service loan taken over forty-five years, they struggled until making the final payment just before Dad died.

Our three-bedroom weatherboard wasn't much, but it was ours. When my second sister arrived, double bunk beds in the two smallest rooms got us by. We were cramped by today's standards, but happy.

As houses continued to pop up, more families moved to the Valley. Eventually it attracted the Dodge City name tag. Many families had problems. Domestic violence was rife with some families having regular police attendance while others visited relatives in gaol. There were also a lot of ex-servicemen and families just trying to get ahead. Mum and Dad didn't discriminate. They got along with everyone. Money was always short, but we didn't care.

One thing the Valley wasn't short of was kids. Nearly every family had a large brood. 'No Pill back then,' as Mum would say. There were regular cricket and football matches, and we would roam the streets and parks making our own fun from daylight until the street lights came on.

In the mid-sixties tragedy struck. Dad's fire station was called to a gas leak at the Cuba Coffee Café in George Street, Sydney. Three gas company employees and the cafe owner lay unconscious in the cellar. Dad took a deep breath before heading down. He managed to drag one to the ladder before collapsing. Dad's mate, Don Wilson, took a breath, pushed others aside and headed down. He lifted Dad to a waiting ambulance before saving the man Dad had dragged over. The other three died.

Dad was in a bad way when senior fire officers knocked on the door. As kids we didn't understand. We were just excited to see Dad's picture on television.

Dad pulled through and eventually went back to work, but things were different. He'd always liked a beer, but now he drank more, a lot more. With it came mood swings and bouts of anger. The fire brigade must have noticed something was wrong. When they sent a medical officer to interview Mum, she feared Dad would lose his job, so she told them everything was fine. It wasn't.

Dad resigned and blew his superannuation. Nevertheless, he always managed to find work. As his drinking worsened, money became scarce. With it came the arguments. Dad would spend his evenings at the pub before coming home late. Dinner plates were upended, china broken and food strewn. By the time police arrived, Dad was usually asleep. Police back then did little before moving to the next call. Our crisis was just another in a sea of domestics.

Times were tough, but not everything was bad. School holidays were spent with Mum's family at Comboyne. My brother and I wandered from farm to farm, helping in the dairy and drinking warm cream from empty beer bottles. For city kids it was great fun. Then there were day trips to Dad's favourites, sightseeing in the Blue Mountains or fishing and swimming at Clovelly Beach.

As Dad aged, his drinking eased, and I found a man I loved. Clever and witty, he had an insatiable appetite for books. He was also a natural comic and would have us, and later on his grandkids, laughing in hysterics. I just wish we'd seen more of that side growing up.

Any kid who went to housing commission public schools in the 1960s and 70s knows what it is like to be bullied. I was always tall and built like the proverbial string bean. That and my quiet nature made me a target for bullies. All wanted a reputation for belting the tall kid. Teachers were preoccupied with figuring out how to get a transfer, so I was left to sort my own problems.

Dad did some boxing in the army and instructed me to put my weight behind my punches. Problem was, I didn't have any weight. In the end I just did my best. By high school I'd had my fair share of bloody noses but managed to hold my own.

Busby High School was on the edge of the Valley, wedged between Liverpool Speedway, Italian market gardens and row upon row of fibro housing. Heading home one day in third form, now year nine, I was king hit from behind by David Buggy, a kid who had been taunting me for weeks. He fitted the small-man-syndrome type, surrounded by mates all baying for blood. With the crowd gathered around us, fighting was unavoidable.

It didn't take long for me to get the upper hand. That's when it happened. A flurry of hits from behind knocked me down. Then came the boots and fists as others joined in. Blood ran down my face as broken teeth punctured my lips and tongue. The kicks kept coming. As I attempted to stand, someone's shoe connected with my head. A golf-ball-sized lump exploded around my eye, restricting my vision. My nose gushed with blood. I tried to lift myself, but couldn't. I could barely move. I realised if I didn't stand up I was in for the hiding of my life. I made another effort, somehow managing to get to my feet. Pushing a few aside I ran as fast as my legs could carry me. Blood plastered across my face and, with one eye closed, I could barely see. It didn't matter. I could hear the mob behind me. I jumped a fence and shot straight past a woman into her house.

'Get out. I'm calling the police.'

Turning, I was relieved to see her yells weren't directed at me, but the thugs behind me in her yard. The woman did her best to clean me up, but I was still a terrible mess. My cuts were stitched at Liverpool Hospital, but there was nothing they could do for my teeth. Mum later spent a fortune we didn't have to get them fixed.

When detectives turned up they assured me they would sort the whole thing, and sort it they did. I didn't see who kicked the hell out of me, but it didn't matter; the detectives found no shortage of witnesses. The ringleaders were arrested and convicted, and those not sent to institutions were expelled. It reaffirmed my desire to become a police officer.

•

I entered the NSW Police Academy at Redfern in 1978 at the age of eighteen. Scraping enough money together, I bought my first suit. It was typical of the era: brown pinstripe, with a mustard shirt and wide tie that screamed 1970s. The Redfern Police Academy consisted of barracks surrounding a parade ground. Decidedly bland, the red brick predated the First World War. Built as a depot for mounted police, the archway off Bourke Street was built high enough to accommodate men on horseback. As the twentieth century progressed, horses gave way to cars, and the depot was refurbished with classrooms. A small number of mounted police remained for ceremonial purposes, relegated to the western block where winter mornings spread the sickly-sweet aroma of horse manure throughout the academy.

Instruction consisted of Acts of Parliament and Police Powers. Reciting lengthy rules and regulations was mandatory. Physical fitness, weapons practice and marching drills were all part of the eleven-week training routine.

Unlike others, I didn't have any connections to serving police to help with a good posting, so I was sent to Central Police Station. As the name suggests, it was in the middle of Sydney. Something of a penalty station for misbehaving police, it was one of the less desirable postings.

Along with twelve other probationary constables from class 159, I reported at Central on a cold day at the end of June. Parading at attention in the courtyard, Inspector Merv Beck welcomed us: 'We have two types of police here at Central: those sent here as punishment and probationary constables. Your job is to keep your nose clean.'

It didn't exactly fill me with enthusiasm.

Central and its cell complex was a tired station wedged to one side of a narrow lane between George and Pitt Streets. The gloomy lane was a contrast to the lights, traffic and crowds of the busy theatre district less than a hundred metres away. The footpath to George Street was too narrow for the purpose it had been built, mostly being blocked by rubbish dumped out the back of businesses. There was no alternative but to walk along the narrow strip of tar that passed for a road.

The station itself was a run-down remnant of the nineteenth century. The buildings, four storeys high, were joined at a right angle to form an L shape around a central courtyard. The whole structure looked to be well past its use-by date. Opposite Central Lane was a bland brick wall holding up an old theatre, given a second lease on life in the 1970s as Maxy's Disco. The station archway bore the scars and gouges of prison vans trying to navigate the narrow turn.

Central's buildings had undergone many alterations over time. Above the courtyard, external metal walkways ran along each floor, lead paint peeling from their cast-iron balustrades. An antiquated elevator operated noisily at the juncture of the two blocks. I soon worked out it was quicker to take the stairs.

The cell complex on the opposite side of the courtyard was cement and iron. Devoid of natural light, it was gloomy and depressing. This would be my home away from home for the next three years.

Before joining, I saw police as upstanding pillars of society – a view that was soon to change. Many at Central were hard working, but others left a lot to be desired. Most were just marking time until their next move.

The culture of police alcohol abuse shocked me. Some drank the entire shift before heading to the pub. It was nothing for the charge-room crew to empty a carton before knock-off. One sergeant kept a six pack on the paddy wagon floor as we patrolled up and down George Street. In the era before PTSD was recognised, I came to understand that for many police, alcohol was the medication of choice.

Over time, though, alcoholism seemed less of an issue compared to other things. Inebriates and others relieved of money contributed to the station drinking fund. Police were quick with fists and slow with questions. The misdeeds were endless.

During this time I still lived with my mum and dad. Travelling to work in uniform wasn't easy. It drew a lot of sneers, even from people with whom I'd grown up. A cop living in the Valley wasn't the norm.

My family copped flak from a few, particularly from Ernie Forman who lived three doors up. My brother and I had grown up with his sons. Ernie was a big bloke who drank heavily. A loudmouth and king-hit bully at the local pubs, Ernie was feared, and not well liked. Having had more than his fair share of run-ins with the law, Ernie made no secret of his dislike for police.

As I walked home from the bus stop, Ernie would yell abuse at me from his yard. He liked to show off for the neighbours. The first couple of times I ignored him, until one night he stood on the footpath outside our house in an uglier mood than usual.

'Come on, you copper cunt. Don't fucking hide in there, come out and have a go.'

I didn't want problems at home, but it was now hard to ignore. 'What's the problem, Ernie?' I said to him. 'We've never had an issue.'

I just wanted him to go home. As he continued to yell profanities, more lights came on along both sides of the street. My brother walked up behind me, followed by Mum and Dad as neighbours came from everywhere.

Ernie grinned. 'I'm sorry, Pete. I've just had too much to drink.' He put his hands up in a gesture of surrender. 'I'm sorry. Are we good?' He held out a hand, and as I went to shake it, Ernie landed a king hit fair on my chin.

Mum yelled, 'You rotten mongrel!'

It took a moment to gather my senses. Telling Ernie he was under arrest provoked little more than a laugh. Then it was on. Neighbours ran from everywhere. Some hoped to see Ernie's downfall, others wanted to see a copper flogged.

When Ernie took up a fighting stance I didn't hold back. My brother had my back, so I knew I wasn't going to be attacked from behind this time. Ernie only landed a couple before I started getting the better of him. When a cut opened over his eye, he put his hands up. 'I've had it. You win.'

As he walked towards me, I didn't take my eyes off him. He then attempted to headbutt me before I landed punch after punch until he dropped.

A few neighbours had given Mum and Dad a hard time since I joined the police, so my brother took the opportunity: 'Has anyone else got an issue? If so, let's sort it now.'

No one said a word. I called the local paddy wagon and threw Ernie in the back. Mum and Dad never had another problem. Humiliated in front of the whole neighbourhood, Ernie thereafter kept to himself.

•

After fifteen months in uniform I became frustrated at not being able to follow through on the bigger investigations. After speaking to Joe Parrington, the man in charge of the CIB at Central, I purchased two safari suits and began training as a detective. As was always the way for younger police, I was excluded from the hushed conversations and the more sinister goings on, gradually exposed until the old guard felt I could be trusted. I learned to steer clear of those who liked to interview with a heavy hand, but not all police were like that. Most played by the rules, but said nothing about those who didn't. Loyalty to fellow police always came first, even if you didn't like what you saw. That was the culture.

After three years at Central I was transferred to Fairfield Detectives before another move, this time to Newtown. If I thought Central was bad, Newtown was a whole new ball game. Corruption was everywhere. I started seriously questioning whether I wanted to remain, before accepting a rotation to the Fraud Squad to give me time to think. The police force wasn't turning out as I'd expected.

Returning to Newtown I distanced myself from a number of events, and I made no secret of the fact I wasn't happy. In what Justice James Wood would label 'The Brotherhood' the culture protected dishonest police, and I felt powerless.

The Brotherhood worked because police not involved in corruption weren't prepared to speak out against those who were. If you did, your complaint went nowhere, and your life became hell. Detective Mick Drury learned that lesson the hard way in 1984, shot through his kitchen window after reporting corrupt police. He lived to tell the tale, but the lesson for others was clear.

A series of ugly events in 1983 forced my hand. I was thinking about throwing the job in, but my dad convinced me to tough it out by applying for a country transfer. I didn't know where I'd end up, I was just determined to get out of Sydney.

'Where's Cessnock?'

The reply was short and gruff. 'Near bloody Maitland. Do you want to go or not?'

After five years in Sydney I was happy to go anywhere. Cessnock turned out the best move I could have made.

In the late 1800s coal transformed Cessnock from a small village to a thriving township. As communities sprang up with new mines from Kurri Kurri to Paxton, the Coalfields were born. With a staunch mentality and defiance, the coalminers were a tough lot whose outlook permeated throughout the community. By 1983, most of the underground mines had closed in favour of open cuts further north, but the locals' stoic demeanour remained.

When I arrived, anti-police attitudes were strong. More than once I was reminded how police shot dead Norman Brown at the Rothbury Mine Riot. The town carried grudges a long time considering Brown died in 1929. It was a tough community where policing wasn't easy. Be that as it may, the move was positive for me, with corruption and repugnant police behaviour now a thing of the past.

Detective Sergeant Ken Snedden, the son of a local coalminer, joined the police force later than most. His age and local knowledge gave him a distinct advantage.

'I know your grandmother, son. She'd be shaking her head if she knew what you've been up to.'

Ken would shame offenders into admitting crimes without a hint of the violence I had witnessed in Sydney. He also went out of his way to help families get wayward kids back on track. It was old-fashioned policing that would have been scoffed at in Sydney. Ken wasn't a big drinker, which suited me fine. His idea of policing revolved more around people. No heavy-handed tactics. No verbals or forced confessions. Just hard, honest policing.

The Coalfields had a higher than average incidence of child sexual abuse. It was a crime where offenders rarely made admissions. Ken had a way around that, offering to get them help to deal with the problem if they owned up. Ken just had that manner about him, eliciting trust, talking compassionately regardless of how he really felt. Often it ended in tears, with Ken getting the admission and saving victims the ordeal of a trial. He never ceased to amaze me, and I never stopped leaning.

Detective Senior Constable Dave Woolnough transferred in from Taree, completing our office of three. Dave had a lot of larrikin about him, which I liked. We became mates and our friendship has endured past our careers. Dave was a very competent investigator with extensive country service. He loved nothing more than locking up crooks. He told me to check the charge book each morning – 'It tells you who the workers are.'

Like me, Dave had little time for lazy police.

'If you're good at what you do, your name should be here [as signing the charge] more than anyone else.'

It was a lesson I remembered. From that time I took pride in a heavy workload. At long last, having just turned twenty-four, I was doing what I loved. I had found my passion.

Even at Cessnock, however, the corrupt side of policing was never far away. When it turned out a crook who was robbing elderly couples was protected by a Newcastle detective, Ken and Dave were fuming. Complaining to the detective inspector at Newcastle, they were told to pull their heads in and were all but kicked out of his office. The Brotherhood wasn't confined to Sydney, but at least I knew on which side of the fence Ken and Dave sat.

Those years were undoubtedly some of the happiest of my career. We did some great investigations with our small team, and I learned from two of the most ethical and professional detectives ever to take an oath. I would model my next three decades of policing on what I learned during that time.

Within months of arriving in Cessnock, I met Penny. A coalminer's daughter and divorcee with a young son, she lived opposite my unit in Abermain. We caught each other's eye with her young son soon asking me over for dinner. That's when we began dating and married two years later, raising three beautiful children.

After Cessnock, I moved to Maitland and Singleton before returning to Cessnock as a detective sergeant in 1993, where I continued investigating a whole range of crimes.

CHAPTER 3

PROTECTING THE BRAND

By 1994 the police force had been dragged kicking and screaming into the state's biggest upheaval since the Rum Corps overthrew the NSW governor in 1808. Police corruption had been festering for decades. John Hatton, a NSW parliamentary independent, had been agitating for an inquiry for years. Honest police were confiding in Hatton about corruption behind the public facade. Hatton voiced concerns but lacked the political might to make things happen. Neither major party was keen to see a wide ranging inquiry into the police force.

In 1994 all that changed. The NSW Liberal National Party (LNP) under the premiership of John Fahey was in a precarious position. As a minority government they needed support from the three cross benchers. John Hatton took full advantage and secured support from his fellow independents. With both major parties courting the independents, all Hatton had to do was bring one of them on board. The LNP and its police minister, Terry Griffiths, were strong supporters of the police force, jumping to its defence whenever the need arose. Hatton realised he would never gain their support.

The Labor Party under Bob Carr was a different proposition. Keen to score political points, they wooed the independents, although they were cautious not to commit to a Police Royal Commission. The Labor Party knew opening Pandora's box carried risks. In an attempt to placate Hatton, Labor agreed to support a censure motion against the police minister. Realising this would amount to little, Hatton rejected the proposal.

Leading up to the next election, Labor's chances of winning were not looking good. With time running short, Bob Carr became desperate to win the independents' support, and in May 1994, he capitulated, committing Labor to a Police Royal Commission. Everything fell into place mostly for political reasons, but Hatton didn't care; at last he had the numbers.

On 11 May 1994, Hatton stood in parliament citing allegations of corruption that had plagued NSW Police for decades. He not only pointed the finger at senior police, but also at Internal Affairs, the very body charged with policing police. Allegations of cover-ups emerged with Hatton tabling information from police whistle-blowers. The LNP realised this wasn't just another Hatton outburst, this time they sensed something was afoot. News filtered to police headquarters. Whatever was going on, it wasn't good. Senior police started making the short dash to parliament in order to lend support to a police minister under siege and intimidate Hatton with their glares.

Parliament launched into heated debates well into the night, but the outcome was predetermined. Hatton had the numbers. As planned, the motion for a Royal Commission into police corruption was carried by the slimmest of margins, forty-six votes to forty-five. Hatton took his seat as a chill ran though police ranks.

The following day, news of the Police Royal Commission splashed across the front pages. It was the lead story as NSW learned that its police force was to be investigated.

While many police greeted the announcement with trepidation and resentment, others quietly applauded. I say quietly because you voiced support at your own peril. Police hierarchy considered the Royal Commission unnecessary, and those who supported it were branded turncoats. Hatton was called a zealot. Police who had confided in him were accused of having axes to grind.

In the early days, the police force still had the backing of certain politicians and sections of the media. As systemic corruption and hundreds of crimes committed by police were exposed, all remaining support wavered, before vanishing altogether. The police force was on its own.

The Royal Commission revealed destruction and fabrication of evidence, with rampant bribery. Evidence emerged of fraud, theft, drug trafficking, protection rackets, standover tactics and serious assaults. Many police faced criminal charges while others resigned in disgrace. I wasn't surprised.

The Police Royal Commission concluded in 1997 with many honest police disappointed. Rampant corruption was exposed from constable to sergeant, but seemed to stop there. Few at the top were identified, or apparently knew what was going on.

When it was all over, the government began searching for a new commissioner to rebuild the force. Englishman Bobby Peter Ryan was chosen.

With the loss of public confidence, Ryan decided to clean out the police force from the top down. His purge was ruthless. Many good police were sacrificed for a supposed clean start. It wasn't. It merely elevated the next level to the top. Eventually the government accepted Ryan's early resignation. Some changes were made, but for the most part the old police force remained.

The Royal Commission also scrutinised police shielding child sex offenders. Notorious paedophile Robert (Dolly) Dunn was identified as one of those protected by corrupt police. Dunn had been a teacher working alongside the likes of paedophile Marist Brother John Chute. In his book, *Dirty Work*, disgraced former Detective Glen McNamara said Dunn boasted of Catholic priests among his cohort. Dunn even wore priestly garments while committing his crimes.

Although the Royal Commission examined Dunn, many questions went unanswered. Operation Retz was an internal police inquiry established to examine why senior police failed to act on evidence against Dunn and his associates. Its report was highly protected. Later attempts by former police officer Tim Priest to access the Operation Retz files as part of his damages claim against the state government, ran into brick walls. In 2006 the Supreme Court sided with Priest when it ordered police to hand over the files. While three hundred pages were surrendered, police continued to withhold documents in breach of Justice Johnson's order. As a storm threatened to erupt, parliament intervened, ordering police to hand everything to the Legislative Council. The three hundred pages suddenly increased to thirty-five thousand overnight.

Charlie Lynn, a Legislative Council member, studied the files and believed at least twenty others were still missing, including a crucial report on Dunn. Powerful politicians and police fought calls for the files to be made public. In 2007 Lynn reported:

Operation Retz provides a disturbing insight into
incompetent and corrupt leadership practices at the

highest levels of NSW Police. The report indicates that these corrupt practices extend into the offices of the NSW Ombudsman and the Police Integrity Commission. The disclaimer indicates that the corrupt leadership culture in NSW Police is much worse than indicated in the report … I believe it was a deliberate attempt to obfuscate the process of the investigation. It was a means of ensuring Operation Retz would be a Clayton's investigation and that the full extent of the corrupt leadership and management practices in New South Wales would never be exposed.

The report remains under lock and key and the files have never been made public.

•

In Cessnock the Royal Commission had little impact. We took an interest, of course, but we were busy getting on with our work. I investigated many family-related child abuse cases, oblivious to the fact that one of the city's most prolific child sexual abuse predators, Father Vincent Ryan, was residing in the presbytery behind Cessnock's police station.

Trainee detective Troy Grant spent time in my detective office at Cessnock in the mid-nineties before moving to Newcastle's Regional Crime Squad. In 1995 two men confided in each other about their childhood sexual abuse at the hands of Ryan. One contacted police. Up until this time investigations into the clergy were few. Troy Grant was assigned the investigation and arrested Ryan at Taree after Ryan's sudden move to that parish. It would later emerge that the Maitland–Newcastle Diocese knew Ryan was sexually abusing boys more than twenty years before his arrest.

With many of Ryan's crimes having happened in my patrol, I took more than a passing interest. Following Ryan's arrest, and with public interest heightened by media coverage, the trickle of abuse survivors coming forward became a flood. More than thirty boys would eventually go to police. Despite paying out more than ten million dollars in compensation, the Maitland–Newcastle Diocese insisted Ryan was an isolated case.

•

One evening in 1989 I was called to investigate a suicide at Kurri Kurri. Teenage suicides were few and far between, but this boy was only fifteen when his body – still dressed in his school uniform – was found by his parents hanging in a tree in the family's backyard. On a personal level, our eldest son, from Penny's previous marriage, was only two years younger than this boy. He attended the same school and wore the same uniform. As I went to sleep that night, I quietly shed tears.

The boy's parents were devastated, and their distress was heightened by the fear that the Catholic Church would not permit their son to be buried in consecrated ground because he had taken his own life. Speaking to the coroner, we couldn't eliminate the boy slipping and accidently becoming entangled; the cause was therefore put down as death by misadventure/suicide, allowing his family some peace.

Decades later I was told the boy's family had been close to Vince Ryan, assisting the priest on Church committees. When Ryan was arrested the boy's father – a former police officer – put two and two together, but by then it was too late. Tragically this boy was not Ryan's only possible victim to take his own life.

•

Commissioner Peter Ryan's restructure of the NSW Police Force in the late 1990s resulted in the closure of many country detectives' offices. My office at Cessnock and those at Maitland and Raymond Terrace were amalgamated into the Lower Hunter Command at Maitland.

With this amalgamation I became reacquainted with Detective Senior Constable Mark Watters. I first noticed Mark working in uniform at Cessnock in the 1980s. He had a voracious appetite for work; the more the better. But it wasn't just his work ethic that caught my attention. He was concerned for people, taking the time to listen and help. It didn't take long for me to convince him his future lay in becoming a detective. In the early 1990s Mark and I parted, however by 1998 Mark was again on my team, this time at Maitland.

The following year a woman I'll call Annette, who will feature significantly in this story, reported having been sexually abused as a child. Now in her fifties, after decades of silence, Annette reported the offences committed against her. The delay was not unusual. Police refer to such reports as 'historical offences'. The Child Abuse Royal Commission would later establish that, on average, it takes a person twenty-two years to report child sexual abuse. As a police officer I wasn't aware of that figure; no one was back then. That sort of research was in the future. I just knew that victims often walked in to report abuse anything up to fifty years later. It was normal and understandable.

A lot of detectives weren't keen to take on historical offences. With no crime scene, no physical evidence and few, if any witnesses, they were difficult crimes to investigate, let alone prosecute. Often it boiled down to the victim's word against that of the accused. Mark, however, didn't hesitate to take on Annette's complaint.

It was my job to supervise Mark's investigations. The fact Annette's abuser was another Catholic priest from the Maitland–Newcastle Diocese caught my attention. After taking Annette's statement and with her preparedness to pursue criminal charges, Mark began the process of tracking down her abuser. What should have been a routine arrest turned out to be anything but predictable. Telephoning the Maitland–Newcastle Diocese, Mark learned that Father Denis McAlinden was believed to be somewhere in England, or then again, maybe Ireland. They really couldn't be sure. In any case, Mark was given assurances they would let him know when Father Mac returned. Having had little previous dealings with the Catholic Church, we both believed they would do the right thing. How naive we were. I now know of no instance in that era when the Catholic Church voluntarily handed over one of its alleged paedophile priests to police.

The Church usually kept a tight rein on their priests, so not knowing McAlinden's whereabouts was unusual. Even more unusual was that they didn't know how to contact him. Mark considered it a temporary setback; after all, the Diocese controlled McAlinden's stipend.

In many ways it was just another investigation with no reason to doubt the Church. After all, if you couldn't trust the Church, who could you trust?

It would later emerge that the Maitland–Newcastle Diocese had, in 1993, paid for a one-way ticket to Britain for McAlinden after other survivors of McAlinden's sexual abuse complained to the Church. To avoid scandal, they moved perpetrators from one parish to another, often interstate. In extreme cases the offending priest would be moved overseas.

McAlinden was an extreme case. But back then, Mark and I still had a lot to learn.

In 1992 McAlinden escaped conviction in Western Australia before being unceremoniously dragged back to New South Wales as more of his victim's began coming forward. The Church could only cover up so many scandals, and McAlinden was becoming difficult. Survivors were no longer content with a Church assurance of, 'Leave it with us. We'll take care of it'.

That didn't cut it anymore. Abuse survivors, supported by the media, were finding a voice and demanding action. Many expected the Church to take their complaints to the police, for criminal prosecutions to commence, but were reticent to act without the Church's blessing.

As a storm loomed over McAlinden, the Church resorted to an old tactic. Why not, it had always worked in the past. They simply moved him. And another unassuming priest carried his bags aboard an international flight.

None of this was known to Mark, to me or to Annette as we looked for McAlinden. Like many survivors, Annette believed she was McAlinden's only victim. Unbeknownst to all of us the Church knew of more, but they weren't saying. I will take you through the detail concerning all of this shortly, but for now it suffices to say the Church said nothing to the police force, Detective Watters, and certainly not to Annette. The full extent of McAlinden's crimes and the Church's concealment of those crimes would only become known to me a decade after Annette came forward.

•

In 1995 Father Philip Wilson, later Archbishop of Adelaide, listened to two women tell of their abuse at the hands of

McAlinden. There was no mistaking what the women alleged. Wilson sat listening, asking questions, ensuring nothing was missed by tape-recording every word. Making doubly sure, he typed it down and had them sign it as sworn testimony.

Leo Clarke knew McAlinden was a serial child sex offender in 1976 when he received a letter from the Diocese's Vicar General, Monsignor Patrick Cotter, just before Clarke's consecration as Bishop of the Maitland–Newcastle Diocese. In 1995, Clarke wasn't just told of the women's abuse as outlined in the statements taken by Wilson, his knowledge went further. McAlinden had admitted to sexually abusing both women as children. Clarke had assured McAlinden his 'good name would be protected'.

It seems to me, that's how the Church operated. Others also knew. But what happened in the Church stayed in the Church. Nothing was volunteered to Mark Watters. Surely someone must have realised McAlinden was a monster, destroying dozens, if not hundreds, of young lives. No one stopped him. His victims were children. Kids from good homes, Catholic homes, homes these men of God served. Christian values cried out, screamed out for someone to do something, to stop him, yet not one of these men of God lifted a hand.

Mark wasn't told that months earlier the Diocese sent McAlinden a letter. An address! They had it, but the Church kept quiet about that too, telling Mark they weren't aware where McAlinden was residing.

Community outrage surrounding Vince Ryan was still high. His case was bad, but McAlinden's was an even bigger scandal – if it got out, that is. On the back of Ryan, it could irreparably damage the Church's reputation in the Hunter. There were two options. They could go to the police with everything. Sure, it wouldn't sit well, but it would show they wanted to rid the

Church of rapists and seek justice for the children abused. The second option was to say nothing, cover it up and hope it would go away. The first option was problematic. It would mean the truth, the whole truth and nothing less. It meant disclosing past knowledge of McAlinden's crimes, not just once, but repeatedly, over decades. Moving him from one parish to another, state to state and overseas. They knew if Detective Watters got hold of McAlinden it would spell trouble for a lot more than just one troublesome priest. Good men of the Church would be implicated in McAlinden's ongoing ability to abuse. The Church determined that could not be allowed to happen.

In 1999 the Diocese had damning files in its secret archives; files documenting decades of McAlinden's crimes. They went back half a century. Worse still, they disclosed that senior clergy were complicit in concealing those crimes, therefore facilitating the sexual abuse of more children.

Clergy had spoken to the families of children their fellow priest had raped. The files also recorded McAlinden admitting what he did to 'the little ones'.

Instead of going to police, the Church sat on the information. More *little ones* were abused and the Church did nothing to stop it. When too many knew, Church tradition dictated McAlinden be moved to another parish. In the meantime, the Church's good name was protected.

CHAPTER 4

A TROUBLESOME PRIEST

The fourth of seven children, Denis McAlinden was born in Ireland in 1922. Attracted to a life in the Church, he began studying at the Redemptorist Limerick Juniorate at the age of twelve.

On Ireland's storm-swept west coast, Limerick stands defiant against the elements. Its church buildings are cold, the grey stone reflecting the harsh weather in that part of the emerald isle. But McAlinden didn't intend to spend his life in the cold of Ireland; his ambition lay in doing God's work in warmer climates. Missionary work with children in Africa excited him.

But McAlinden's excitement wasn't shared by his superiors. They took issue with certain aspects of his behaviour. Sexual misconduct was never mentioned in a 1940's letter by receptionist, Father John Treacy, to the Bishop of Maitland when endeavouring to transfer McAlinden, but McAlinden's behavioural issues and unsuitability for living in a religious community were raised. Something wasn't right.

In 1949, after fifteen years of study, McAlinden was ordained as a priest. His behaviour, however, remained problematic.

The Redemptorists saw something they didn't like, enough to want to rid themselves of their newly fledged protégé.

Despite McAlinden's desire, they weren't prepared to send him unsupervised to the missions in Africa. But the Church had invested much in this man. So, what to do? He needed to be placed somewhere, preferably under supervision.

The Redemptorist Order had established itself in the NSW Hunter Valley in the 1880s. Australia was therefore a viable prospect for McAlinden. Many problematic Irishmen had already been sent to this foreign shore, so what was one more? Better still, they had a connection. Maitland's Bishop, Edmund Gleeson, was also a Limerick-trained Redemptorist. On the other side of the world, Australia was well out of sight.

Father Treacy was a man of many talents. Skilled in the written word, he had a way of making the unattractive seem appealing. Penning a letter to Gleeson he asked if there was 'any possibility of taking one of our students'.

Reading Treacy's correspondence it is clear that he went to great lengths to sell McAlinden. He told Gleeson that McAlinden was 'difficult', adding, 'You will very justly say then: What is wrong with him ... why do you not wish to retain him?'

Treacy explained that McAlinden didn't fit community life and was better suited to a Diocese. Eager to rid themselves of their troublesome priest he concluded: 'Hoping you will be able to send word soon about whether you can see your way to accept Denis McAlinden.'

Not knowing of the 'behavioural issues', Gleeson did accept McAlinden. It was a decision that would result in immeasurable harm for the Hunter's children.

•

Arriving in the Hunter, McAlinden's interest in young girls was soon apparent. There was, unfortunately, no going back. Incardinated to the Maitland Diocese, he was now its responsibility. As crimes against young girls accumulated, McAlinden was shuffled from one Hunter Valley parish to the next, leaving behind a trail of tears and innocent lives destroyed.

Complaints began as early 1951, with a young girl sexually abused in McAlinden's Tighes Hill confessional. After another incident following a swim lesson, a tactic McAlinden would regularly employ over the coming decades, an eleven-year-old girl told her mother that Father McAlinden had put his hands inside her swimmers. The horrified mother slapped her daughter's face, telling her she was 'wicked and evil'.

Blind faith caused the little children to suffer. McAlinden was moved.

In 1953 when the parents of a ten-year-old Raymond Terrace girl discovered McAlinden had abused their daughter, they complained to Bishop Gleeson. No, it wasn't just touching, he had put his penis in her. Their little girl had been raped. It wasn't isolated, McAlinden had been raping her repeatedly since she was nine. Bishop Gleeson didn't tell police, but he did send the parents a letter saying the Church would take care of it. McAlinden was moved again.

Encompassing the Hunter and much of the Manning Valley, the Maitland Diocese would later become the Maitland–Newcastle Diocese. It was big, with large distances between parishes. Nevertheless, constantly moving McAlinden was becoming tricky. The Upper Hunter was fast running out of new parishes as McAlinden's appetite for young girls knew no bounds. From Murrurundi to Muswellbrook, Singleton to Greta, word was spreading. Quietly, secretly, there were rumblings. Nothing loud, you understand; good Catholics didn't speak ill of a priest. It was drilled into them from childhood. Everyone knew that a priest was God's representative on earth. To speak ill of a priest might bring eternal damnation. Even so, on sports days or parish get-togethers, conversations happened. Parents whispered not to leave kids alone with a certain priest. There was a look. Yes! That look. No more needed to be said.

McAlinden never stopped applying for the missions. Working with children in Africa still excited him. By 1958 he had managed to gain the support of Romolo Carboni, the Pope's Apostolic Delegate to Australia. Following Bishop Gleeson's death, the job of managing McAlinden fell to Maitland's new Bishop, John Toohey. In an unusually candid piece of correspondence, Toohey voiced opposition to Carboni, raising McAlinden's motives, which he 'preferred not to state'.

Within the Church things are often known but not spoken of, and rarely put in writing, so this letter to Carboni provided a unique insight. Carboni appeared to grasp the letter's cryptic message. McAlinden remained where he was.

Toohey made it clear to McAlinden that 'serious obstacles' prevented his working in the missions, telling McAlinden he was aware of his 'previous misconduct'.

Another might have given up, but not McAlinden. His desire for the missions was overpowering, a calling if you like. It took ten years, but he finally got his way. When he was caught sexually abusing young girls from his Greta parish, the Diocese was limited in finding somewhere new in which to place him. McAlinden was therefore sent to Mendi in the highlands of Papua New Guinea for four years. No supervision, just McAlinden and the local population.

With tensions in the Hunter easing, parishioners were told McAlinden was doing God's work with children in the tropics. The news must have been received with mixed feelings.

Following an undisclosed incident, McAlinden was moved to a more remote village, causing Bishop Toohey's right-hand man, Father Patrick Cotter, who would later be bestowed with the title Monsignor, to speculate, 'His change while in New Guinea from Mendi to Mt Hagan must have been for some reason.'

From New Guinea, Bishop Firmin Schmidt wrote to Toohey:

I have received letters from people in his area, indicating he has been very rough with the native people in recent months, and thus they thought it would be good for him to get out of the area.

By 1973 McAlinden's time in New Guinea was up. Toohey wanted him supervised, so appointed McAlinden as an assistant priest. McAlinden wasn't happy; he didn't want another priest looking over his shoulder. Two years later, as Toohey lay dying, McAlinden again got his own parish.

•

Forster–Tuncurry is a popular tourist destination. An idyllic coastal community surrounded by sea as it straddles the turquoise waters of Wallis Lake. With Denis McAlinden's arrival, paradise was about to be lost. Free of supervision, the troublesome priest soon fell back into old habits, with parishioners complaining about 'Father McAlinden and the children'.

Some protested to the Catholic Education Office about McAlinden's conduct. When nothing happened, a delegation of parents met with Father Francis Coolahan, one of the Diocese's more senior priests, demanding McAlinden's immediate removal. McAlinden was at it again, touching young girls, they explained. Learning of the allegations, Monsignor Cotter recorded: 'These charges have to do with "de sexto" in an unusual way, but I think not extremely serious.' Cotter wasted no time travelling to Forster and interviewing up to a dozen parents. The truth was all too plain and irrefutable. He didn't record if he still considered the allegations *not extremely serious* as the community demanded McAlinden's instant removal, but he did note: 'He has lost all credibility – the children are scared of him … in the circumstances he himself should not want to stay in the parish.'

The gum and eucalypt trees lining the Pacific Highway must have become a blur as Cotter's mind raced faster than the landscape. Parents had made it clear the Church needed to act, and act now. As a defender of the faith his priority was clear. Sure, what happened was terrible, but now the Church's good name was at stake.

Hastily convening a meeting of Diocese consultors, Cotter told them that God's other work would have to wait. Some would not have been happy abandoning prepared dinners. Good home cooked meals would go to waste.

If Cotter's fellow priests weren't happy, too bad. He wasn't going to carry all this on his own. He needed help. Cotter got straight to the point. They had a problem, a serious problem. McAlinden. No more needed to be said. They knew what Cotter meant. Knowledge of McAlinden's crimes had previously been confined to one or two parents, making it easy to contain. The problem this time was that many parents knew. Worse still, one parent was a lawyer. Grumbling stomachs now gave way to worried looks. This was serious. Just before he died, Bishop Toohey had reminded them all of the Church's oath of secrecy. Going to police was not an option. In the short time he had been in charge, Cotter had managed to keep the lid on Vince Ryan's crimes. The truth about Ryan would not become known to police for another two decades. Normally these matters were dealt with by the Bishop, but with Toohey's death, Cotter had been temporarily thrown in the deep end until a new Bishop could be appointed.

The consultors placed McAlinden on leave. That was easy enough. The tricky part was where to move him next. By now he had caused so much damage across the Diocese it was impossible to place him anywhere. One thing was certain: he could not be sent back up to the Hunter Valley. That was why he had been sent up the coast to Forster. Now, that too had been ruined. There was no choice, he would again have to leave the Diocese.

Beyond transferring him, what else could they do? The Church's canon law acknowledged the inherent sinfulness of clergy abusing children, but only required McAlinden to be rebuked and given warnings. They had tried moving him, which also failed. Canon law also dictated that a priest's good name be protected, and secrecy was demanded by *Crimen Sollicitationis*, a 1962 Holy Office instruction, which American priest and academic Thomas Doyle would later describe as 'an explicit policy to cover up cases of child sexual abuse by clergy'.

McAlinden's crimes were again concealed. A pontifical secret.

Melbourne's Leo Clarke was appointed Maitland Diocese's next Bishop. In a letter dated 7 May 1976, which I touched upon earlier in this story, Monsignor Cotter informed Clarke of McAlinden's latest transgressions. It is not known when Clarke came into possession of McAlinden's extensive file, which detailed his earlier crimes, but as you'll read, he did take possession of such a file. Cotter told Clarke that McAlinden was 'a man of very good faith and pastoral hard work', before explaining:

> Fr Mac has an inclination to interfere [touching only]
> with young girls – aged perhaps seven to twelve or so.
> The furore cause[d] by striking the boy about the head
> in the presence of the whole class caused the girls to give
> the other information to their mothers which they had till
> then withheld. On examination this is found to be factual.
> Having dealt with the people I had a long session with
> Fr Mac at the presbytery. Slowly very slowly he admitted
> some indiscretion but then agreed that it was a condition
> that had been with him for many years. He feels no such
> inclination towards the mature female but towards the
> little ones only. There never has been any physical assault
> or damage but inevitably it leaves a psychological scar
> on the child's mind and attitude and religious outlook.
> Fr Mac finally came to the point of asking me to try
> to arrange some treatment for him. He is willing to
> resign his charge of the parish – beginning to feel some
> embarrassment saying mass & preaching. I have never
> heard of this condition before and knowing Fr Mac as we
> do, we think it cannot be real serious, nor do we believe
> that there is any danger of a development into assault or
> rape. At the same time what has been going on is more
> than can be tolerated.

The letter is a damning indictment on Church thinking, not only for the attitude to clergy crimes but also for what is missing: concern for the children. Despite saying that McAlinden's behaviour *leaves a psychological scar on the child's mind,* Cotter failed to raise the subject of the children's welfare. All concern was reserved for Father Mac.

Cotter suggested moving McAlinden to Western Australia until he could be discreetly slipped back into the Hunter some time later. McAlinden looked forward to the move. Another fresh start. In his letter to Clarke, Cotter explained: 'The reason Father wants to go so very much now is because it will afford a good cover-up for his resigning the parish.'

Even back then, the Church never shied away from calling it what it was: a cover-up.

In closing, Cotter turned to McAlinden's treatment. McAlinden could stay with family until his move was arranged, he said. As an endnote he apologised for his handwriting, explaining to Clarke he couldn't risk having it typed and others seeing his letter. He went on to tell Clarke that the Church's coat of arms for Clarke's ordination had arrived. Together with eighteen bishops and the *papal nuncio* confirming their attendance, his letter ended on a happier note.

McAlinden didn't make it to Western Australia. Instead he was sent for another stint in New Guinea. In 1981 he was quietly slipped back into the Hunter, although his feet barely touched the ground. With Western Australia seriously short of priests, Clarke seized the opportunity to write to Bishop Thomas in Geraldton: 'there were some problems [with McAlinden] that I mentioned to you but as I said in Sydney, I think that these problems are now over ... I would really think he is worth a try. If I didn't I would certainly not be suggesting that you take him.'

McAlinden was sent to the remote Pilbara, its isolation to his liking. After abusing more young girls he was again moved two years later.

Sent to Tokomaru Bay in the south-east of New Zealand's North Island, McAlinden wrote to a young girl back in the

Pilbara saying he missed her, before unexpectedly fleeing back to Australia. Bishop Edward Gaines from New Zealand's Hamilton Diocese told Clarke, 'He [McAlinden] took off in rather a hurry.'

In 2008, Gaines' successor in the Hamilton Diocese, Bishop Denis Browne, confirmed that McAlinden 'was guilty of sexual offences' during his time in New Zealand.

McAlinden's sexual abuse of children now stretched to a third nation, yet the Church still didn't go to police. After three and a half decades of knowledge concerning McAlinden's crimes, the Catholic Church continued to fail its children by inflicting the same priest upon even more unsuspecting families.

CHAPTER 5

FIGHTING AGAINST THE CURRENT

As scandals in the Hunter settled, McAlinden was able to sneak back home. After postings in Dungog and Morisset, he was moved again.

Where the Golden Highway arches across a colourful patchwork of fields to Mudgee and beyond, Merriwa sits as a stunning grain and sheep-farming district on the extreme north-western fringe of the Hunter Valley. The town has a long association with the Catholic Church. The Sisters of St Joseph Convent, St Joseph's Primary School and St Anne's Church all share a parcel of land on the northern edge of town. Denis McAlinden's presbytery suited his desires perfectly. Naivety could no longer be an excuse – senior clergy knew of McAlinden's attraction to, and crimes against, children well before placing him in a presbytery located right next to a school.

Saint Mary MacKillop, the nun who established the Sisters of St Joseph, once held an Irish Catholic priest, Father Ambrose Keating, to account for sexually abusing children in his Kapunda parish north of Adelaide in South Australia during the 1870s. Mary MacKillop upset Church hierarchy by demanding something be done. How dare she, a woman, tell them what to do! The offending priest was, however, moved to a parish back in Ireland; clearly, relocating paedophile priests was not unique to the twentieth century. For her troubles, MacKillop was all but excommunicated, something the Church still tries to play down. After her reconciliation with the Church, Mary's Order expanded in 1885, opening a school in Merriwa, and the Josephite nuns were still teaching there over a century later, in the mid-1980s, when their relationship with another Irish priest became strained.

The children trusted their nuns and told them things, even when Father Mac said it was a secret. Confrontations followed, but the status of women in the Church was still well below that of priests. The nuns knew it, and so did McAlinden. Something more had to be done. When the school's principal – a nun – reportedly complained about McAlinden to a more senior Josephite nun, she never returned whilst McAlinden remained.

Mike Stanwell replaced the nun as principal. At the start of 1986 he remained ignorant of his predecessor's complaints. Others knew but said nothing. Mike, therefore, had no idea what he was walking into.

Mike and his family were regular churchgoers and quickly developed a friendship with McAlinden. He was soon invited to their home for meals and family mass.

McAlinden took full advantage of his proximity to St Joseph's Primary School, visiting often and unannounced. He delighted in walking through the playground dishing out sweets to kids as they excitedly clambered all over him. It excited McAlinden too, but in a different way. His behaviour didn't go unnoticed, but the nuns and teaching staff felt powerless.

Mike remained ignorant of the sinister nature of McAlinden's sojourns into his school until a day in April when Mike arrived early. The grounds were quiet at that hour, before parents began to drop kids off and the children's squeals enveloped the playground. Mike enjoyed their noise. He loved his job and the kids. The quiet morning gave him time to reflect and take in the cool air. The chill of winter hadn't yet arrived, but you could feel it coming. It was a pleasant transformation from the blistering heat of summer when the leaves hung from the trees in wilting exhaustion. Now they stood upright in welcome relief, vibrant, embracing the seasonal change.

St Anne's Church is twenty metres from the school, standing as much a tribute to artisans of a bygone era as a place of worship. Rough-hewn sandstone decorates the walls inside and out. The stone now shows its age, but that doesn't detract from its natural beauty with pinks, golds and tans radiating through time. They contrast with the rich red of the ceiling, a legacy of when timber was more abundant in those parts. On such a glorious day, Mike could feel his Church beckoning. He looked at his watch. There was still time to sit with God.

Mike walked casually between the buildings as the church's steep roof loomed tall in the growing light. That's how churches are intended to be: when you walk into God's house, you are supposed to feel small. Mike walked in quiet reverence, blinking to adjust his eyes from the light outside. He expected the church to be empty but he sensed a presence. There, halfway down the pews, sat Father Mac with a little girl from year two or three. Thinking she might be there for confession, Mike left quietly.

Back in school, Mike thought more about it, visualising the scene. The girl wasn't next to the priest, she was on his lap. The realisation made Mike uneasy. Why didn't it register before? Perhaps it was being caught off guard when he had expected the church to be vacant. That was another thing –

apart from the priest and child, the church was empty, completely empty. Mike was troubled. He tried telling himself it was all innocent, but he couldn't get the image out of his mind. He hadn't seen McAlinden do anything wrong, but still the picture troubled him. He thought about McAlinden handing out lollies, encouraging kids to climb all over him. The priest started to fit the image all mothers warn their children about. And why were the nuns and other staff so cold towards this priest?

By morning recess Mike could no longer contain his apprehension. He decided to talk with his staff. They had been there longer and knew McAlinden a lot better. Speaking to two lay teachers, Mike began awkwardly. It went against the grain to speak ill of a priest, even to suggest it.

Neither teacher would look at him, which made Mike all the more uncomfortable. Both women kept looking at each other as if to say, *Will you tell him, or will I?*

They weren't sure if Mike could be trusted, worrying he might jump to the priest's defence. As Mike revealed what he had seen, they realised they were on the same team. All was quiet before one spoke. Although they were alone, she spoke softly, as if God himself might hear.

'You're not the first one to see things like that. It's been going on for a while.'

Awkwardly they explained the former principal's attempt to do something. Mike understood their anxiety. From what he gleaned, the Church wasn't prepared to do anything beyond replacing anyone who complained. Mike believed he hadn't seen enough to go to police and didn't feel doing so would be supported by others without the Church's blessing. He was in an unenviable position. Even so, he didn't need to think long. It might cost him his job, but the kids came first.

Mike ran ideas past his staff, including nuns who hadn't yet warmed to a principal who wasn't one of their own. They all supported him. After the demise of their former principal, staff again had hope.

The next morning Mike stood at an assembly and told the children they were not to go into the church before school. Nor were they to go to the presbytery or take lollies from Father Mac. At a Catholic school this was unheard of. Heresy, no less. He knew his action would eventually get back to parents and Father Mac. It was also inevitable the Catholic Schools Office would learn of it.

Mike prepared himself for the backlash. Not one parent objected, at least not openly. The Schools Office was never told, or if they were, said nothing. What is certain is that someone told the priest.

McAlinden never spoke to Mike about his announcement, but their friendship came to an abrupt end as the priest began subtly attacking Mike during homilies. Without exchanging words each knew where the other stood as teachers and nuns kept a close eye on the children. Mike knew that McAlinden was just waiting for an opportunity.

Mike also knew that he was risking his career, but he had to do something. He confided in colleagues, but all baulked at the idea of going to the Bishop. There had been stories about McAlinden for years, they warned. They reasoned Bishop Clarke had to know.

One suggested Mike speak to John Hatton, the politician who would later spark the Police Royal Commission. Mike weighed it up before deciding to chance it with the Bishop. He couldn't believe the Church knew and would knowingly put children at risk. Mike would later tell me he should have gone straight to Hatton.

Bishop Clarke was a busy man. A week went past before he could see Mike. Having placed McAlinden at Merriwa, Clarke may have guessed the reason for Mike's visit. Pleasantries aside, Mike got to the point, telling Clarke about McAlinden and the girl on the priest's lap. Mike also imparted damning stories he had learned from staff. He expected Clarke to be alarmed, shocked, dismayed. Instead the Bishop appeared detached. Hearing stories of children being sexually abused seemingly moved him no more than a weather report. It wasn't the reaction Mike expected.

Clarke spoke calmly. 'This isn't the first time I have heard of McAlinden's activities.'

His friends had been right about the Bishop knowing, but still Mike was relieved. At least he wasn't shown the door. Clarke didn't say what he knew, but assured Mike, 'I will be doing something about this, but it may take some time before I can have him placed somewhere for rehabilitation.'

Mike had expected to argue, even plead or beg. It now seemed all too easy. He was convinced the Church would investigate, even go to the police. Now Mike needed a drink. A few colleagues keen to hear the outcome joined him, but instead of acclaim, they poured scorn on Mike's optimism. Nothing would happen, they told him. Mike prayed they were wrong.

April turned to May and nothing occurred. With June just around the corner, it was getting cold. Mike worried his colleagues might be right. When a nun asked to speak with him in private, Mike's stomach churned. The look on her face told him it wasn't good. She had spoken with two eight-year-old children.

'They went away somewhere with Father McAlinden on the weekend, and Father McAlinden bathed them both.'

One told the nun Father Mac had 'touched her, down there'.

Mike boiled with anger. Clarke knew they couldn't keep an eye on McAlinden forever. A devious man, it was inevitable he would find a way around their vigilance. The longer the Church dragged its feet the more likely something like this was going to happen. Now another child had been abused while the Church dithered. Clarke's words, *This isn't the first time I have heard of McAlinden's activities*, reverberated in Mike's ears.

Clarke knew and did nothing. In Mike's mind, that made Clarke just as culpable.

Ropable, Mike started his car. If the Church wouldn't act on his say so, then maybe it would listen to the child's parents. Together, he thought, they could force the Church to act. Mike took deep breaths to quell his rage as he pulled up outside their property. How do you tell parents a priest has sexually abused their daughter?

Mike knew the parents. They were good people, good Catholics. Both listened, but refused to believe. Father Mac wouldn't do that, they told him. No matter how hard Mike tried, he couldn't break down the wall. McAlinden was a priest, touched by the hand of God. Their faith wouldn't let them even contemplate it. Overstaying his welcome, Mike left dejected. Without the parent's support, going to police didn't seem an option. Still he refused to give up. Phoning Clarke's office, he was told the Bishop would not meet with him; he would have to speak to the new Vicar General. Mike was angry. Considering the gravity of the situation, he believed that Clarke should have been dealing with this personally.

Mike made the three-hour drive to Maitland, this time to meet with the Vicar General. Raised in Cessnock and educated at Sydney's esteemed St Joseph's College, Philip Wilson was ordained in 1978 before teaching at St Pius X High School in Adamstown and undertaking religious studies in Washington DC. After eight short years, he had risen to become Bishop Clarke's right-hand man and was reportedly destined for even greater roles.

Philip Wilson listened quietly as Mike went over what he had discussed with Clarke. Mike didn't ask and Wilson didn't say if the Bishop had told him of his earlier meeting with Mike or briefed him on the matter, but things were now worse. Mike left nothing out as he searched Wilson's face. There was no reaction.

Looking Wilson square in the eye Mike told him, 'I believe that this did happen as the girl has indicated.' Mike made it clear he wanted something done right away; he did not want to wait until another child was harmed.

Wilson gave Mike an assurance: he would personally investigate the allegations.

Wilson travelled to Merriwa that week, asking Mike for directions to various homes. Mike would later tell me when Wilson returned he said, 'I spoke to the child's mother, and something has definitely gone on.'

McAlinden would be removed, Wilson told Mike. Did it mean a criminal investigation? Having contemplated approaching police himself, Mike was now confident the Church would do so.

True to his word, no sooner had Wilson left than McAlinden was removed. The relief for Mike and his staff was palpable. Some parents were puzzled by their priest's sudden departure, but not all. One was visibly upset. Her pain would remain well after McAlinden left.

After McAlinden's removal … nothing. That was it. McAlinden was again moved to reside near another school, this time in Newcastle's Adamstown parish. Mike was dismayed. How could they do that when the Church acknowledged that something had definitely gone on.

Bypassing the Church, Mike phoned the Adamstown principal with McAlinden being moved again. Decades later Mike discovered he had been too late, telling me a former student from Adamstown confided in him that McAlinden had grabbed her hair, pulled her into the confessional box and sexually assaulted her.

•

McAlinden wasn't referred to police. In 2010, as Archbishop of Adelaide, Philip Wilson defended his handling of the McAlinden case, saying he suggested to a Merriwa mother and to Mike Stanwell that they go to police, 'but they were very hesitant'.

Wilson also noted he couldn't go to police, because no one was prepared to make a statement. Mike, on the other hand, publicly rejected both of Wilson's assertions: 'That is not true. I was prepared to make a statement. He never asked me for a statement, but I would not have hesitated if he had. I was more than happy to take this to the police.'

In 2010 Mike provided police – me – with a signed statement.

The whole experience left Mike disenchanted with his Church and with the Catholic Schools Office, which only spoke to remind Mike that the Church signed his pay cheques.

Mike Stanwell's assertions were supported in 2003 by a former Merriwa student who told police that families of McAlinden's victims told Church authorities of abuse and, 'The victim's families were told not to bother police with these matters and they [the Church] would take care of it.'

•

When Father John Gahan arrived in Merriwa he seemed ignorant of his predecessor's removal. Not only did Mike Stanwell tell Gahan what occurred, he warned him that children remained at risk. When Mike said he was thinking about approaching John Hatton regarding McAlinden, he said Gahan warned him: 'The Church can deal with those matters, and going to someone like that will only damage the Church's reputation. To do so will only bring scandal on the Church.'

Mike told me he never approached Hatton, but it turned out someone did. Hatton was told all about McAlinden's removal from Forster and Merriwa, and in 1987 he wrote to Cardinal Edward Clancy in Sydney:

> There have been several complaints about his behaviour with young children and there exists a great deal of concern at his continuing access to young people. But the great difficulty facing me and you is the reluctance of people to come forward, particularly if they feel that they will be the subject of some form of suppression or retaliatory action within the Church structure. As you can see, it is a problem of great worry to me and only after considerable thought have I decided to bring it to your attention, on a strictly confidential basis, to avoid any injustice and to avoid any reflection upon the Church. I genuinely feel from the people with whom I have discussed this matter that if an assurance were given that they would in no way be victimised they would speak out frankly and the evidence could be obtained. I know of no other way of handling this matter to avoid embarrassment and to have the problem corrected other than by this very confidential approach directly to you.

Hatton's role in securing the Police Royal Commission made him a hero to many, myself included. That said, learning in 2013 of his letter to Cardinal Clancy left me dismayed. *Avoid embarrassment ... avoid any reflection upon the Church ...* allowing it to handle the matter *on a strictly confidential basis.* Hatton wasn't Catholic, but his actions in handing the matter to the Church instead of police left me more than saddened.

Hatton's plea for no reprisals fell on deaf ears. Subtle at first, many in the Church and school community distanced themselves from Merriwa's outspoken principal. Mike's health deteriorated, but his attitude of putting children ahead of the Church remained steadfast. Years later, Mike was sacked after he struck Father David O'Hearn during a heated argument. Mike returned to teaching after winning an unfair dismissal case, but never returned to his principal's position. O'Hearn, as you will hear, would go on to be another priest exposed for serial child rape.

Having attracted unwanted attention, McAlinden was sent for psychiatric evaluation. With Hatton taking an interest and more than one child sexual abuse scandal on its hands, the Church needed to act, or at least appear to be doing something.

Within months of Hatton's letter a child abuse seminar was planned by two of the Church's rising stars who you will hear a lot more about later, Fathers Brian Lucas and John Usher. Dates were fixed, presenters organised and a venue sorted. Then, it was decided that the seminar couldn't go ahead because it was 'too close to the special function for Cardinal Freeman's eightieth birthday'.

Those were the Church's priorities. Perhaps the seminar could happen next year.

While the Church dithered once more, McAlinden was sent to see Dr Derek Johns. It seems from their conversations

Dr Johns learned that McAlinden was first disciplined for touching children as early as 1954. Further reprimands followed. McAlinden chatted about his fondness for handing out lollies and his missionary work in New Guinea where, he said, he became, 'a little over-familiar with children'.

Even so, McAlinden maintained he had done nothing wrong. It was a misunderstanding. Children misinterpreted him, that's all.

Dr Johns' report to Bishop Clarke ruled out any major psychiatric disorder: 'The long period of time over which these alleged incidence[s] have taken place on a recurring basis, certainly makes one suspicious as to Father McAlinden's intent, as does his apparent difficulty in learning from experience, and his absolute denial of ever having experienced any form of sexual interest in his life.'

Clarke's reply was perplexing: 'I am very grateful to you for working with Father McAlinden and helping him. I can only hope that he benefits from your professional interest and concern.'

That was it. A few visits and his paedophilia was supposedly cured. Clarke moved McAlinden to another parish, this time in Nelson Bay.

Despite Dr Johns warning of McAlinden saying he was *a little over-familiar with children* in New Guinea, Clarke tried to slip McAlinden back to Australia's former colony. This time New Guinea Wewak Diocese's Bishop Raymond Kalisz was wary, sending Clarke a carefully worded letter. 'I presume that he doesn't have any serious defect of character that would be disruptive of the community?'

Clarke emphasised McAlinden's denials, but was forced to disclose that the Church knew of credible complaints regarding young victims in the recent past. Although Clarke did concede,

'It would be a charity for some Bishop to take him on knowing the problems that have arisen.'

Fortunately for the children of PNG, Bishop Kalisz wasn't feeling charitable, and declined Clarke's request. The Maitland Diocese would have to find another solution.

•

McAlinden's crimes were so widespread, it was impossible for him to remain in the Maitland Diocese. It was therefore decided to send him back to Western Australia, but not anywhere near the Pilbara. This time he was sent to Bunbury in the state's south-west.

In 1991 McAlinden's past caught up with him when he was arrested for indecently assaulting a young girl when he was back in the Pilbara. When many still considered men of the cloth infallible, she somehow gathered the strength to tell police. It was her word against the priest. In 1992 McAlinden was found not guilty, but at least she had confronted her tormentor and had her day in the Perth court. It sent a message. Child abuse victims were finding a voice.

CHAPTER 6

SEEING THROUGH THE CRACKS

Leo Clarke looked older than his sixty-nine years. Managing a Diocese plagued by priestly crimes can have that effect. Church policy dictated child rape remain a secret. As its obedient servant, Clarke played his role.

In 1992, as Denis McAlinden faced a Perth court, the ABC-TV's *Compass* program broke new ground with 'Ultimate Betrayal', a story about clergy child sexual abuse. It caused quite a stir, with Father John Usher being among the first to jump to the Church's defence. Anglican Archbishop Peter Hollingworth, who would later resign as Australia's Governor-General after an inquiry revealed his own failures to deal with allegations of child sexual abuse, supported Usher by calling the story preposterous. But it was too late; walls had begun crumbling, and people were seeing through the cracks.

After 'Ultimate Betrayal', abuse survivor Rod Stinson spoke to the ABC, resulting in another story, 'Conduct Unbecoming'. The focus this time was a secret protocol with the Church insuring itself against abuse-handling failures while keeping everything in-house by using Catholic Church Insurance. Considering the Church's assertion of encouraging the referral of all child sexual abuse to police, the need for insurance provoked questions. As early as 1988, in a confidential church briefing note Father Brian Lucas rightly predicted: 'What the media will search for is the cover-up, or the failure of the Church to act appropriately.'

Lucas was right. But an unforeseen spin-off of all this media attention was the snowballing effect of encouraging more abuse survivors to come forward. With their voices no longer silent, it put the Church under ever increasing pressure.

•

Anthea Halpin and her sister, Denise Laverie, will now become the two most significant figures in this story. When Anthea read a 1992 newspaper account of Denis McAlinden appearing in a Perth court, she was shocked. Not by the sexual abuse allegation, but because a woman had the courage to speak out. Back then that sort of thing was rarely heard of. Despite his acquittal, Anthea believed the woman's allegations. Reading the article over the phone to her sister, there was quiet before Denise replied, 'I believe it.'

Anthea took a deep breath. 'I do too.'

It may have been the pause, the way the words came out, or just being sisters, but nothing further needed to be said. Both knew. Until then, neither had been aware the other had also been sexually abused by their uncle, Father Denis McAlinden.

Over time, Anthea and Denise opened up to one another about their abuse. There was anger as well as tears. Despite the verdict they knew the Perth charges were true. After all, Uncle Denis did the same to them. If the Church had known about their abuse, could it have helped the woman in Western

Australia? They weren't to know the Church already had a substantial dossier on McAlinden going back decades. WA Police were never told. It remained hidden, a secret under Canon Law, carefully guarded in Bishop Clarke's archives.

Sister Paula Redgrove had been friends with Denis McAlinden for years, which is how she got to know Anthea and Denise as children. In addition to being a nun, Sister Paula was a good woman, and the girls trusted her. So it was that Sister Paula was the person Anthea told of their abuse as well as the abuse of two other girls. Sister Paula believed them before asking another woman, who she knew associated with McAlinden as a child, if McAlinden molested her too. When Barbara (not her real name) confirmed Sister Paula's worst fears, she became the fifth victim Sister Paula knew about.

At Sister Paula's behest, Barbara went to Bishop Clarke's office in Maitland, where she met with Monsignor Allan Hart. There was no surprise shown at Barbara's disclosure. Hart explained the Church already had similar stories from Merriwa and Taree. Clergy knowledge of Denis McAlinden's crimes was widespread.

Clarke of course knew all about McAlinden's crimes well before Allan Hart told him of the latest. With rumblings of victims going to the media, Clarke realised he needed help. If journalists started digging, these latest complaints against McAlinden could expose the whole sordid mess. Clarke knew that couldn't be allowed to happen and made an urgent phone call to Sydney.

Allan Hart, meanwhile, told Barbara the good news: the Church was prepared to investigate. However, statements would be required. The Church investigator was a legally qualified lawyer as well as a priest. A man highly regarded within the Church, his position was still a mystery, sitting on the periphery as he operated in the Church's shadows. Barbara was told he would contact her. Before he called, at the urging of Sister Paula, Barbara spoke to her long-time friend, Linda (not her real name). Barbara was horrified to learn Linda had also been sexually abused by McAlinden. The list of known victims continued to grow.

•

Although part of the Sydney Archdiocese, Father Brian Lucas seemed to have a roaming commission. He was the Church's voice on everything from euthanasia to papal rituals; his other skills, however, were not made public. When it came to 'special issues', the euphemism for dealing with child sexual abuse, he was the Church's go-to man. Lucas would later be described as one of the main architects of Towards Healing and the Church's approach to dealing with clergy sexual abuse.

A solicitor before becoming a priest, Lucas saw things through the eyes of a lawyer. With canon law demanding child sexual abuse files be guarded in a secret archive, Lucas travelled to the United States and Canada to see how they handled things there. It would later emerge that the Boston Diocese contemplated diplomatic protection by sending child abuse files to the *papal nuncio* or Vatican, safeguarding them against law enforcement.

Armed with new ideas, Lucas returned to Australia, warning Church hierarchy that their secret archives might not be safe. He went on to give speeches with titles such as 'To shred or not to shred – is that the question?'.

He wasn't referred to as the Church's Mr Fix It for nothing. In certain circumstances, Lucas noted, the Church could hand documents to its lawyers thereby attracting legal privilege and making them inaccessible at law. By 1990, he had become the Church's main advisor on 'special issues'.

Child abuse policy wasn't the only skill for which Lucas was renowned. He had a gift, a special gift: if anyone could get a paedophile priest to confess, it was him. I would have loved someone like him on my team, but then again, maybe not. Confession or not, he never passed anything on to police, nor wrote anything down. That was his policy. No crumbs were to be left for others to follow. By the time Bishop Clarke rang Lucas in 1993, the latter had built up quite a reputation.

When Lucas phoned Barbara, things didn't play out as she had imagined. There was no easing in or priestly compassion. Business-like, Lucas fired questions; to her he was cold and insensitive, more like an inquisition. Barbara thought Lucas was taking notes for a statement – that's what Monsignor Hart said the Church required. Lucas would later maintain he never took notes, ever. He relied on his memory for everything Barbara told him, including victim's names, phone numbers, dates, places and, of course, the details, the awful details. It was quite a memory. She felt terrible when Lucas asked for her friend Linda's contact details. Now she feared Linda would be subjected to the same insensitive interrogation.

Lucas's call ended as abruptly as it began. There was no thank you or apology. Lucas was only interested in the facts, the brief facts. Detail didn't matter. With Lucas's questions fired in quick succession, Barbara didn't get a chance to ask if the Church was going to report her case to the police. Lucas never asked her if she wanted the Church to go to the police, of that she was sure. In a few minutes he was gone. Barbara hoped to read and sign her statement, but if one was made, she never saw it. But that wasn't the end of Barbara's story.

•

After his Perth acquittal and developments in Maitland, McAlinden barely had time to settle back into Western Australia before being recalled. Bishop Clarke kept the reason secret, telling the Denmark/Mount Barker parishioners it was due to McAlinden's ill-health. Mother Church had always protected him. If McAlinden felt any smugness it would have disappeared when Clarke removed his priestly faculties. If that hurt, it was meant to. In a letter to McAlinden, Clarke told him, 'Certain serious allegations have been made.'

The direction to get himself to Sydney to see Lucas must have put the fear of God into him. McAlinden failed to catch his flight, disappearing for a few weeks, eventually surfacing at Taree on the NSW mid-north coast. During this time, Barbara remained in contact with Hart and Lucas. Having befriended Philip Wilson, Barbara said she also spoke to him about the matter over the phone whilst he was still in Washington. She wasn't happy about McAlinden's disappearance, but continued to place her faith in the Church dealing appropriately with the matter.

Not everything about Lucas's meeting with McAlinden is known, but Lucas did manage to squeeze admissions out of McAlinden. We know this not because the Church passed those admissions on to police, but because, according to documents later obtained by a NSW Special Commission of Inquiry, they were reported to Bishop Clarke and Catholic Church Insurance: 'their complaints were referred to Fr Brian Lucas. He handled this case with great dexterity & exacted a confession from the priest that he offended'.

When Lucas phoned Barbara, the news wasn't all good. McAlinden had admitted to abusing Anthea, Denise, Linda and others, but he couldn't remember Barbara. Lucas had apparently overlooked Barbara's maiden name. As a child, it was the only name by which McAlinden knew her. When Barbara pointed this out to Lucas she was understandably angry. Lucas overlooking this denied her any chance she had of closure. In a heated exchange with Monsignor Hart, Barbara threatened to go to the media. Instead, outraged, disappointed and emotionally drained, she walked away wanting nothing further to do with the Church investigation. I can't help wondering, was this what the Church intended?

Forcing McAlinden into retirement, in 1993 the Church bought him a one-way ticket to Britain, with instruction not to return. McAlinden agreed, but it wasn't long before he reneged on the deal, his desire for children too strong. He never intended to dwell in purgatory for long.

McAlinden may have been told his priestly faculties were removed, but he remained a priest. Without McAlinden's consent he was not able to be defrocked. The Church remained an antiquated institution with rules favouring its men of the cloth, regardless of their crimes. Travelling to Ireland, McAlinden then secretly made his way to the Philippines on his own initiative. McAlinden again worked as a priest after approaching a Filipino Bishop and failing to disclose his suspension and past history. He was on leave and volunteered his services. With so many poor children in need of God's help, McAlinden created his own heaven.

When McAlinden's nieces discovered his whereabouts, they were furious. In an attempt to placate them, the Church promised to have him defrocked; anything but go to police. McAlinden refused to cooperate with the defrocking process, but agreed to return to Australia. That said, it took Bishop

Clarke more than a year to get McAlinden home, and when he did, McAlinden soon disappeared into Western Australia.

At the Diocese's request, Sister Paula Redgrove asked Anthea and Denise if they would provide statements. Both wanted McAlinden stopped and if that meant making statements, so be it. Neither sister knew Barbara, so were unaware she had walked away after the Church's earlier botched handling.

On Tuesday, 10 October 1995 Anthea and Denise concealed where they were going, telling their mother they were off shopping. In truth they drove to the Diocese's head office at Hamilton. After years of failing to prevent McAlinden accessing kids, the Church was finally going to the police. The monster was finally going to be stopped. At least that's what Denise thought.

Spartan in appearance, the interview room within the Diocese's Hamilton complex was devoid of religious paraphernalia. It spoke formally. Amid sparse furnishings sat an enormous table. To the outsider the room was unwelcoming. Philip Wilson had just returned from studying canon law in Washington DC. Dressed in priestly regalia, Anthea and Denise thought he added to the officially chilly atmosphere. Denise couldn't remember the name of the other priest that day; Wilson appeared frightening enough. Anthea was re-directed to the door. She wasn't exactly told to get out, but it wasn't far short.

Denise was now without support. She recalled what struck her more than anything was Wilson's detached manner. Already on edge at watching her sister leave the room, things continued to slide downhill. Denise remembered the meeting as devoid of compassion, empathy or pastoral care. Didn't they realise what she had been through? What they were asking? Secrets so painful they had been suppressed most of her life. Now she was being subjected to a cold cross-examination.

Had it been anywhere else she might have got up and left. The trouble was, her Catholic upbringing forbade her. Denise was still submissive before the Church. Nervous, uncomfortable, she just sat there, scared.

Wilson's face was stern as he picked up a bible and handed it over the table. He wanted Denise to swear an oath, but that wasn't all – she also had to pledge to tell the truth, in writing no less. Did they think she would lie about something like this? Hadn't McAlinden already confessed to Lucas? Denise didn't question Wilson. If nothing else, it was a reassurance of the legal process, or so she thought. No doubt about it. This time they were going to the police.

When Wilson picked up a microphone, Denise froze. Her heart filled with dread as her eyes followed the cord down to a tape recorder. No words of comfort or support. Silence broken only by a click of buttons. Reels turned. A magnetic tape spun monotonously, spooling itself from one side to the other. Denise didn't feel like a survivor telling her story, or even a witness. As Wilson lifted the microphone, she felt like a criminal under a spotlight. So the interrogation began. Those awkward, invasive questions. Wilson spoke with what Denise interpreted as cold detachment, but for Denise her answers were the hard part. Wilson's manner just added to her distress as he asked what, for most of her life, she had tried to forget. Back to being a little girl, helpless and vulnerable. Wilson sat with authority on the other side of the table, that big table, making her feel even smaller. Once more she was powerless before the Church. Wilson asked one question after another, pausing only to hold the microphone over the table. Denise was transfixed as her mind drifted back to being a child and being abused.

With the click of a button it was over. Minutes that seemed an eternity. Denise felt herself shaking as Wilson asked her to leave and send in her sister. They were given no time to comfort one other.

After her interview, Anthea was just as devastated. Both sisters left traumatised. The Church never called to check on their welfare. If this was how survivors of clergy sexual abuse were treated, no wonder so very few came forward.

The day after the sisters were interviewed, police arrived in Taree to arrest Vince Ryan for his crimes against two boys. He would eventually be convicted for offences against more than thirty victims.

Having spoken to Bishop Clarke the day before his arrest, Ryan knew police were coming and called Brian Lucas for advice. Police soon discovered Monsignor Cotter knew of Ryan's crimes as far back as 1974–75. After Ryan's arrest Cotter wrote to Clarke; 'We have had a troubled week with the media turning the screws on us mercilessly.'

Parents were rightly angry with Cotter. Even so, he was unrepentant, writing to Clarke years later: 'I ask myself whether, even if I had direct evidence, would I have reported it to police. Probably not. In the context and circumstances of today – yes; of twenty years ago, probably, no, I think I would have tried to keep it in-house.'

This was said despite Ryan's admissions to Cotter in 1975, following which some of Ryan's victims went on to take their own lives. I know I investigated one of those suicides.

With Ryan's arrest splashed across the news, the last thing the Diocese needed was Anthea, Denise and Barbara's allegations against McAlinden adding to the scandal.

When the Church informed Anthea that her statement was somehow deleted from the tape recorder and she would have to do it all again, it very nearly caused her to walk away.

Trying to avoid another scandal, Bishop Clarke pleaded with McAlinden to accept the laicisation process: 'I beg you, for the sake of souls and the good name of the Church, to cooperate in this matter … this whole matter will be in your good interests as I have it on very good authority that some people are threatening seriously to take this whole matter to the police. I hope you will cooperate in every way.'

McAlinden was defiant. He could afford to be – he knew that Bishop Clarke had his hands full with Ryan. As for going to the police, McAlinden knew the Church would do everything to prevent that. He had them over a barrel. The failure of senior clergy to report his crimes over four decades dwarfed any cover-up of Ryan. Allowing police to become involved would implicate too many senior clergy and scandalise the Church. He had no intention of cooperating.

Three days after their initial interviews, and two days after Anthea's second interview, the sisters were called back to sign their statements. Despite being *their* statements, they were denied a copy. Denise would remember the process as cold and intimidating. It was the last time they would see Wilson for decades.

How much Bishop Clarke really knew about the scale of clergy sexual abuse in his Diocese isn't certain, but it was undoubtedly a lot. As the walls crumbled further, Clarke suddenly retired. His replacement, Bishop Michael Malone, would later say Clarke had been in relatively good health and he 'was out of there like a rocket'.

As Clarke passed the large Bishop's pectoral cross over the table to him, Malone asked, 'Aren't you going to show me where the skeletons are, where the secret things are?'

Clarke pointed to a briefcase in the corner of the room and said, 'Oh, you will find out about that.'

Malone was the fourth consecutive Bishop to keep a dossier on Denis McAlinden's crimes safely locked in the archives. McAlinden's sexual abuse of children was known for more than half a century, yet, year after year, no one went to police.

•

Denise wanted to ask Philip Wilson when police would contact her, but she was too afraid. She took it for granted they would be in touch.

Promoted to Wollongong, Wilson became Australia's youngest Bishop. With Wilson leaving and Clarke's retirement, Anthea and Denise had no idea who to contact. As weeks and months ticked by, Anthea and Denise heard nothing, not so much as a phone call. After everything they had been through, reliving their sexual abuse and the ordeal of lodging a complaint, their hopes for justice now evaporated. They had been abandoned by the Church, forgotten. Like Barbara, they had been treated so badly they just walked away.

When my colleague Mark Watters called the Diocese about Denis McAlinden in 1999, the Church remained silent. Not one word about any of McAlinden's known history was passed on to police.

CHAPTER 7

A LIGHT IN THE CHURCH'S DARKNESS

Despite the police investigation into Denis McAlinden stagnating, pressure on the Catholic Church was unrelenting. It was difficult to keep a lid on so many scandals at once. Every so often one or another had to boil over. Events in the Hunter weren't isolated. Just as Philip Wilson was promoted to Bishop of Wollongong, that Diocese was dealing with its own child sexual abuse scandal.

Like Spencer Tracy's character in *Boys Town*, Father Maurie Crocker tried to keep boys off the streets in the working-class suburbs of the Illawarra. Crocker started by opening a boxing gym at Berkeley, a ninety-minute drive south of Sydney. A hard man with tattoos and a passion for boxing he didn't fit everyone's idea of a priest, but then Crocker wasn't your average priest; he joined the priesthood after careers as a soldier and teacher. Perhaps becoming a priest later in life is what made him different. He carried few illusions about the world.

In 1989 a boy confided in Crocker about being sexually abused by Brother Michael Evans and Father Peter Lewis Comensoli, not to be confused with his cousin, Melbourne

Archbishop Peter Comensoli. (All reference to Comensoli in this story relate only to Peter Lewis Comensoli and not the Archbishop of Melbourne.) The boy wasn't Evan's and Comensoli's only victim. Five years earlier he had complained to Bishop William Murray, but nothing eventuated, so Crocker went to see Bishop Murray himself. Despite assurances to act, nothing happened again.

Dismayed by the Church's paralysis, Crocker urged the boy to go to police, promising to go with him. Cocker in fact provided police with his own statement. Another two boys came to Crocker with similar complaints. Police now had three statements implicating the same clergymen in child sexual abuse, yet police and the DPP decided the matter would go no further. There wasn't enough evidence, they said. Crocker was astounded, and even more so when one police officer refused to even contemplate that a priest could do such things.

The Church learned about police rejecting the boys' complaints. Seeing what they were up against, Crocker refused to stay quiet as he continued badgering police. It proved futile.

Three years later, in August 1992, Operation Paradox, a state-wide child sexual abuse operation, received further complaints alleging Comensoli and Evans were sexually abusing boys. A file was sent to Wollongong Detectives for investigation. Despite the earlier complaints from Crocker and the boys, police reported neither clergyman had been adversely known. The investigation ended before it began.

By 1993 the Church and police had put the matter behind them, and Crocker realised they needed another approach. After some discussion, the boys and Crocker went to the media.

•

Like Bishop Wilson, Peter Cullen was raised Catholic in the Hunter Valley town of Cessnock. Educated at Maitland Marist Brothers, Cullen began his newspaper career as a cadet with the *Maitland Mercury*, eventually becoming editor of the *Illawarra Mercury*. Maurie Crocker, knowing Cullen's reputation for fearless journalism and a strong moral compass, realised Cullen was his man.

Calling in Brett Martin, one of his chief reporters, Cullen spoke to the boys at length. Like Crocker, he believed them. Their accounts were credible enough for the *Mercury* to run a ground-breaking story on 27 October 1993, 'Brother, Parish Priest Molested Us'. It was a brave undertaking, with their story splitting the community. Cullen and the *Mercury* were simultaneously applauded and condemned. Despite some readers threatening to abandon the newspaper, Cullen refused to yield.

Tipped-off before the story broke, Bishop Murray invited two priests mentioned earlier in this book, Brian Lucas and John Usher, to visit Wollongong to interview Comensoli. Again the Church was allowed to investigate itself. No notes were made about their discussion. Lucas also interviewed Wollongong's Father John Nestor about similar allegations (though a court case was later dropped against him). Again he wrote nothing down. The Child Abuse Royal Commission would later find, 'An outcome of Father Lucas's practice was to ensure that there was no written record of any admissions of criminal conduct in order to protect the priest and the Church.'

After the story broke in the *Illawarra Mercury*, Lucas met with the abused boys. What happened at that meeting would later result in controversially conflicting evidence.

Through all the adversity, Peter Cullen stuck by the boys, publishing follow-up stories resulting in more victims coming forward. Under ever-increasing pressure, police were finally forced to act. Brother Michael Evans cheated justice by committing suicide before charges could be laid. Peter Comensoli was convicted before Judge Angela Karpin for crimes against two boys. In a courtroom packed with fellow clergy and parishioners supporting the priest, Comensoli was gaoled for two years with a minimum eighteen months to be served. A third religious, Brother William Hocking, was also arrested and received 150 hours community service for sexually abusing another boy at the same youth refuge where Evans and Comensoli committed their crimes. The boys hadn't altered their evidence, so what had changed? The answer was simple: the bravery of one priest, the courage of journalists, and the pressure of public scrutiny.

•

Following the arrests, clergy closed ranks against Maurie Crocker. According to Crocker's friends Jim Walsh and Vito Gaudiosi, Bishop Murray sent priests to tell Crocker to stop supporting the boys. Knowing right from wrong, Crocker refused.

With police failure and Church inaction remaining unexplained, Crocker contacted the same Police Royal Commission I mentioned in earlier chapters. The Wollongong saga was serious enough to be allocated its own case study. One boy testified that during the meeting with Lucas, 'Well, he [Lucas] stated he would prefer it if we hadn't gone to the *Illawarra Mercury*. He also stated he would prefer if we didn't go to the police and he would deal with it.'

In evidence, Lucas didn't hide his disdain for the *Illawarra Mercury*, accusing it of inflaming the situation. Had the boys approached Bishop Murray in 1993, Lucas argued, it could have been handled differently. Quite a statement considering Murray's previous inaction after the boy first approached him in 1984. Lucas conceded telling the boys he would have preferred they hadn't gone to the media, but denied urging them not to go to police.

•

As further scandals surfaced, Peter Cullen and the *Illawarra Mercury* were more than vindicated. Their critics were shamed into silence. Bishop Murray retired only days before giving evidence to the Police Royal Commission, with Philip Wilson arriving to deal with the ongoing crises. Wilson brought with him a wealth of experience. He would need it. In 2017 the Child Sexual Abuse Royal Commission would reveal that 11.7 percent of priests in the Wollongong Diocese were alleged child abusers, a staggering figure of one in nine.

In the witness box Bishop Murray conceded that in 1984 he met a boy who complained of being sexually abused. Murray accepted he did nothing, arguing he didn't realise the boy was making a formal complaint and he didn't want to disrupt Brother Evans' preparations for becoming a priest.

Although not substantiated, there was talk of a senior police officer running interference for the Church during the investigation. Justice Wood, presiding over the same Police Royal Commission initiated by John Hatton and mentioned in chapter three, was nevertheless scathing: 'Police investigations in each case had all the hallmarks of undue deference to the Church, and were less than thorough or impartial.'

Among a myriad of concerns, Justice Wood cited a failure of police to use intelligence or search for further victims previously unknown to police. Police were embarrassed by the *Illawarra Mercury* showing them how it was done; the ongoing media encouraged further abuse survivors to come forward. The example for police to follow was thus established.

Although primarily focused on police corruption, Justice Wood's Police Royal Commission's examination of the failure of NSW Police to deal with clergy child sexual abuse brought about change. It established the Child Sex Crimes Squad with greater resources, analysts and intelligence officers to identify crime trends and patterns. Justice Wood's message was clear: police had to stop deferring to the Church.

•

For exposing the Church, Father Maurie Crocker paid the ultimate price. There's always a price. Crocker and Vito Gaudiosi became mates when Crocker trained him to the 1991 Australian middle-weight boxing title. Vito later told me that when Crocker returned from a Church conference in 1997–98, he looked 'pissed off'.

Crocker explained that a fellow priest had approached him and said, 'How could you dob in a brother?'

Crocker had replied, 'No paedophile is a friend of mine.'

Such attacks weren't isolated as clergy continued turning their collective back. As the ostracism intensified, Crocker withdrew and became depressed. On 26 March 1998, Father Maurie Crocker was found hanging from a boxing-bag chain in his cherished gym. When I spoke to Vito in 2017, he had no doubt about what led to his friend's death.

Many of those whom Crocker had helped attended his memorial mass. Vito listened as priests who had turned their back, deserted him, or simply saw evil and did nothing, spoke in Church of his friend in flowery tones. Unable to tolerate the hypocrisy, Vito exploded, telling them what he thought in language colourful enough to make a wharfie cringe. Many of Crocker's boys inwardly applauded as the Church service shrank into silence.

Vito and others wept at Crocker's grave. For the Church it was an ugly episode, the less said the better. Despite Vito's request to the Church, there would be no monument or shiny plaque to commemorate Crocker's courage. Crocker's light was the Church's darkness, and they could do without a reminder. The Church allowed Crocker's cherished gym to become dilapidated and eventually demolished.

Archbishops George Pell and Denis Hart attended Bishop Murray's lavish funeral in 2013. Murray's eulogy was full of praise for his loyalty to the Church. His body was laid to rest beside the Wollongong Cathedral. A fitting memorial to a defender of the faith.

From Crocker's humble grave on the other side of town it is impossible to see the Cathedral. I think Maurie would prefer it that way.

CHAPTER 8

TOWARDS HURTING

While Wollongong and the Hunter were going through their ordeals, the Catholic Church in Victoria faced its own crises. In 1995 Father Michael Gannon was gaoled for raping children throughout Melbourne, while Father Gerald Ridsdale was gaoled for similar crimes throughout Bishop Ronald Mulkearns' Ballarat Diocese. A 1993 photograph of then Bishop George Pell accompanying Ridsdale, one of Australia's most notorious and prolific paedophile priests, to court for the first of many trials would become synonymous with the Church's support of criminal priests.

Wollongong's lessons were repeated when media accounts of Gannon and Ridsdale encouraged more survivors to come forward, creating a snowballing effect. Each survivor coming forward emboldened others to do the same, knowing they were no longer alone. The Church reacted by pointing an accusing finger of sensationalism at the media. Child rape and its cover-up wasn't the issue, it was the media's fault for reporting it.

Rumblings sounded of further clergy child sexual abuse around Ballarat, but for now, Bishop Ronald Mulkearns was keeping a lid on it.

Priest rapes child!

Words that make most shudder. It does me, no matter how often I hear it.

For the Church, such words are too confronting, the picture too disturbing. It prefers softer words, gentler words, like 'errant priest', 'lapse of ministry', 'unfortunate', 'isolated' or 'regrettable incident'. Words can obscure, diminish, sanitise, making the crime almost palatable, removing the image, the shock and the outrage. This was the strategy. Church phrases and prearranged scripts posed as media releases, and were then regurgitated by supportive media commentators. By the late 1990s only the most devout were buying it. Victim support groups such as Broken Rites and Blue Knot Foundation helped raise awareness about what was happening. It had taken a long time, but finally the pendulum had swung and the Church was on the back foot. It was losing the moral high ground and, with it, control.

As the number of clergy abuse cases grew, many asked: had the Church concealed these crimes?

Calls for a Child Abuse Royal Commission in the state of Victoria made that state government uneasy. In 1996 Premier Jeff Kennett met with George Pell, Melbourne's newly appointed Archbishop.

Calling Pell in, Kennett told him, 'Now, you clean this thing up and there won't be a Royal Commission.'

Like Hatton, Kennett effectively handed responsibility back to the offending institution.

•

Final approval for the Catholic Church's national Towards Healing protocol was scheduled for November 1996. It was designed to address clergy sexual abuse, supposedly giving survivors a voice and offering compensation. However, Towards Healing also meant remaining outside of police, state and judicial processes and left everything, including investigations and prosecutions, entirely in the hands of the Catholic Church. Archbishop Pell, however, was intent on implementing his own protocol, with lawyers given a deadline of October. There was kudos in being first. With little time to prepare, Pell's lawyers hastily consulted the architects of Towards Healing.

For years, Archbishop Pell had been part of the Australian Catholic Bishops Conference overseeing the drafting of Towards Healing. Now, at the eleventh hour, he was gazumping it. Many saw it as undermining a national approach. If Archbishop Pell wanted his way, Adelaide priest Father David Cappo asked, could he at least hold off until after the launch of Towards Healing?

Father Brian Lucas was more alarmed at a part of the Melbourne Response suggesting the reporting of child abuse to police. He told Archbishop Pell's lawyers that if a priest admitted in certain 'circumstances' to the abuse of children, it would be unfair to pass such admissions on to civil authorities.

Pell's push may have been one-upmanship, prudent business or an attempt to placate Kennett. It may have been a combination of all those things and more. In any case, Pell ignored Father Cappo by announcing his Melbourne Response before Towards Healing. Pell was first, and would forever be lauded as such by his supporters. Towards Healing was approved weeks later. It wouldn't be long before flaws appeared in both.

•

Father Frank Derriman sexually assaulted young girls in Brisbane. In 1967–68 he sexually abused fourteen-year-old Joan Isaac, and when Joan's mother's complaint to Church authorities was passed on to Archbishop Patrick O'Donnell, Derriman was moved to another parish. When another young girl became pregnant, Derriman fled Queensland altogether.

Joan told no one about her abuse other than her husband, Ian, and her mother. In 1996, unable to cope with the secret any longer, and with Ian's support, Joan went to police. Derriman was tracked down living in Ballarat, Victoria. After his extradition, Joan went through the gruelling ordeal of giving evidence, resulting in Derriman being convicted and gaoled. For Joan, that should have been the end of her torment. Instead, it was just the beginning.

After Derriman's conviction Joan asked the Church for an apology under its Towards Healing protocol, not just for her abuse, but for the Church's failure to act. None was forthcoming as the Brisbane Archdiocese manoeuvred to avoid legal liability. The Church's insurer warned Joan that if she pursued the matter through the courts, she would forfeit all pastoral communication under Towards Healing. Effectively: take what we offer, or nothing.

Joan had grown tired of kowtowing to the Church. After commencing legal proceedings, the Church's lawyers sent Joan the following: 'In our view it is clear that the parties have different understandings with respect to the Towards Healing process and protocol.'

The Church considered compensation appropriate for medical expenses and the like, but not for her suffering. If Joan continued, the Church threatened to fight.

In her book, *To Prey and to Silence*, Joan spoke about Towards Healing: 'The Church needed to convince people that they were horrified by the sexual abuse in the Church and wished to address the needs of the suffering victims. In reality, there was no concern for victims. The priority was to save face in the public's eyes and to protect the huge financial fortune that the Church possessed.'

In 1999 Paul Ransley from Channel 9's *Sunday* program was putting together a documentary on clergy abuse and Towards Healing, and asked Joan if she would take part. She consulted Ian, and they agreed it was an opportunity to unmask the truth behind Towards Healing. The program included other survivors Dave Owen and Stephen Woods. All three would one day give evidence about their treatment to the Child Abuse Royal Commission.

When the program went to air on 21 November 1999, the station switchboard lit up with callers outraged at Towards Healing and the Church's treatment of survivors. The Church wasn't happy, citing it as another example of media sensationalism.

By contesting every component of Joan's claim, the Church dragged out her litigation. By 2001, Joan was emotionally exhausted and financially drained. Against Church wealth and expensive lawyers, Joan never stood a chance. When a miserable sum was offered, Joan had no alternative. Demoralised and shattered, she had nothing left. Joan gave evidence to the Royal Commission that when she told Archbishop John Bathersby their offer would disappear in her legal debt, he replied, 'That's your problem.'

For anyone thinking of taking on the Church, Joan's case sent a clear message: the Church wouldn't just win, it would crush any opponent. Having beaten Joan, the Church now put the boot in, insisting she sign a deed of release. The devil was in its detail. Joan had to agree 'not to make any disparaging remarks or comments ... in relation to the subject matter of the proceedings or this settlement to any party'.

Joan could say nothing about her abuse to anyone – journalists, family, friends, even her husband. It was the final humiliation. Her psychologist wrote to Archbishop Bathersby on the impact of silencing an abuse survivor. Bathersby never replied. Church lawyers, however, wasted no time telling Joan to 'refrain from contacting our client'.

Ignoring their warning, Joan wrote to Bathersby herself, pleading, 'I have spent nearly half a lifetime hiding my abuse and living with fear that others would not accept me if they knew of my past. It has been a major breakthrough in my healing that I can now accept myself as I am and to trust that my close friends will do the same. The support and compassion I have received from those trusted family and friends has been truly critical to my current emotional well-being.'

Joan reminded Bathersby of a statement he made three years earlier: 'The Church wants an open environment where the victims of abuse are encouraged to talk openly, and begin the long journey to complete healing with the help of professional counsellors, family and friends.'

Bathersby never replied.

Church lawyers threatened Joan: if she didn't sign the deed of release they would seek legal costs, leaving her financially ruined. She had no choice. Where Derriman failed, the Church succeeded. They destroyed her. After legal costs Joan was left with precious little.

'Frank Derriman had used his power and his threats to silence me as a child and now the Church used its power and its threats to silence me as an adult ... After two and a half years of Towards Healing I was left broken and I was silenced forever ... I suffered for many, many years.'

The Child Abuse Royal Commission heard similar evidence from other abuse survivors, such as Jennifer Ingham and another abuse survivor given the pseudonym DG, who, under Towards Healing, was sent for repeated psychiatric assessments after the Church insurer's lawyers wanted further information. It wasn't about welfare, but money. Like Joan, DG felt Towards Healing was more about minimising financial damage to the Church and less about his welfare.

Yet another abuse survivor, DK, told the Child Abuse Royal Commission of his dealings with the Church between 2010 and 2013: 'I had put my trust back in them for Towards Healing … It's the same abuse. I don't call it Towards Healing, I call it "Towards Hurting" … I feel that the whole Towards Healing process was a sham. I feel a lot of rage in relation to Towards Healing; it is one of the biggest scars in my life.'

Behind the facade, Towards Healing was used as a weapon without pity against abuse survivors. Broken Rites' website cautions abuse survivors against using Towards Healing.

•

Archbishop Pell's Melbourne Response was now up and running. Melbourne was where Emma and Katie Foster had been victims of horrific child sexual abuse at the hands of Father Kevin O'Donnell. Her parents believe Katie started binge-drinking around her second year at high school. A year or so later, at the age of fifteen she ran in front of a car and suffered a debilitating brain injury, requiring twenty-four-hour care for the rest of her life.

Like Denis McAlinden, the Church knew about O'Donnell's offending as far back as the 1940s. Instead of putting children first, it concealed his crimes while moving him from one parish to another. With each move, more children were abused. No one can be sure of the number, certainly dozens, if not hundreds, including Emma and Katie.

Their parents, Chrissie and Anthony Foster, gave evidence that they met with Archbishop Pell in 1997 to discuss Emma's abuse. Church officials organised for the meeting to take place in a presbytery storeroom. The Fosters were crammed onto a wooden bench while the Archbishop sat in an oversized red leather chair. Chrissie described Archbishop Pell as having all the traits of a bully, confrontation his best friend as he threatened, 'The Church's liability would be defended in court.'

At the meeting, the Fosters were supposed to share their pain and receive pastoral care. When told how O'Donnell abused their daughter, they remembered how Archbishop Pell snapped back, 'I hope you can substantiate that in court.'

Anthony sat in disbelief, wondering if the Archbishop was listening, really listening. All Anthony wanted to do was explain the hurt. It seemed all the Archbishop wanted to do was defend the Church. Anthony explained, 'We are victims. Can't you understand we feel that way – can't you understand that many people feel that way?'

Nothing, the room was devoid of empathy.

The experience was so unsettling, Chrissie never got to open the folder she had so carefully prepared. She wanted to talk about her girls, her precious girls. Instead the folder sat there, frozen, gripped behind white knuckles. Before this man of the cloth, her Catholic upbringing overruled her. It refused, forbade, her to speak. The folder stayed closed.

Anthony moved the conversation to the Melbourne Response when Pell cut him off mid-sentence: 'If you don't like what we're doing, then take us to court.'

Archbishop Pell appears not to have consulted survivors' families before implementing his Melbourne Response, and he showed no intention of listening now. Chrissie and Anthony didn't want conflict. Anthony tried to explain that, but the Church wasn't in a mood to listen. Towards Healing or the Melbourne Response, it didn't matter. When the Church's assets were at stake, it would threaten litigation with the best lawyers money could buy.

The meeting ended in disappointment. The Fosters simply couldn't get through. When first called to serve God, did Archbishop Pell really believe this is what God wanted? Anthony would later describe Archbishop Pell as having a 'sociopathic lack of empathy'.

Anthony gave evidence that, in a last-ditch effort, he produced a photograph of Pell presenting Emma with her confirmation certificate. He next showed one of Emma's many suicide attempts, blood streaming from her wrists. Archbishop Pell reacted coldly: 'Mmm ... she's changed hasn't she.'

It was the closest he came to compassion.

Anthony told him, 'This will go on forever. Now, will the Church come to the aid of Emma?'

Pell replied, 'I don't know.'

Anthony hit back, 'You don't know? All the emotional problems Emma will have for the rest of her life will stem from this.'

Anthony was right. Emma continued to struggle as her parents took the Church to court. True to Pell's word, the Church's lawyers fought them at every post. Chrissie and Anthony did everything parents could do, but the damage was too great. Emma took her own life in 2008 aged just twenty-six. Her parents grieved another life stolen by the Church.

•

Whether Towards Healing or the Melbourne Response, the effect was the same: leaving the Catholic Church in charge. With abuse survivors dealt with under Church protocols through the Church's insurance company, damning documents would stay unseen. With civil litigation minimised, the scale of clergy abuse remained hidden from the public. Both protocols advantaged the Church.

•

In January 2002, the *Boston Globe* published a ground-breaking story later made famous by the movie *Spotlight*. Hundreds of horrendous clergy child sexual abuse cases were exposed. More than that, it revealed Church cover-ups on an unprecedented scale. The paper trail led all the way back to Cardinal Bernard Law.

The Boston Globe also exposed a 1985 confidential report revealing the past power of the Church: 'Our dependence in the past on Roman Catholic judges and attorneys protecting the Diocese and clerics is gone.'

By February 2002, the *Boston Globe* reported that a further three hundred abuse survivors had come forward since its story first broke. The Church once more accused the media of smearing its reputation.

Like the *Illawarra Mercury*, the *Boston Globe* published story after story, with the trickle of survivors becoming a flood. Despite Cardinal Law's power within the Church and his position within Boston where more than half the population was Catholic, the *Boston Globe* named him as one of those involved in the concealment of child sexual abuse crimes.

In 1992, a decade before the *Boston Globe* story, Cardinal Law announced a new protocol he said would aggressively deal with abuse allegations. When the protocol proved hollow, District Attorney Thomas Reilly commented, 'He [Law] was basically saying, "Trust us, give us the benefit of the doubt, we'll create a commission to make sure this doesn't happen again." Well, we tried that. It didn't work.'

Father Brian Lucas visited the United States in 1992 and again in 1996 as he helped put together the foundations of Towards Healing. The Melbourne Response and Towards Healing would prove just as hollow as Cardinal Law's protocol.

The *Boston Globe* reported: 'Prosecutors, judges, and politicians who once looked the other way when it came to the Church's dirty laundry are now holding the Cardinal and other Church leaders to a higher standard.'

Noticing a significant number of clergy recorded as being on sick leave, the *Boston Globe* looked deeper, revealing that many of those listed faced allegations of child sexual abuse. This was the Church's way of concealing the scale of the problem. Bishop Clarke had told parishioners in Western Australia that Denis McAlinden was recalled for 'health reasons' and placed him on sick leave. Broken Rites' website is littered with similar accounts of paedophile priests in Australia recorded as being on sick leave. Different continents, but the same scheme. I can't help wondering, was it just coincidence?

His part in decades of child sexual abuse cover-ups no longer a secret, Cardinal Law resigned. Now he needed to escape the glare of those wanting to hang a millstone around his neck. Mother Church came to his rescue, providing refuge behind the Vatican's walls until his death in 2017.

•

On the other side of the Atlantic, Ireland was discovering its own clergy child sexual abuse scandals. Credit again belonged to the media, this time with a television program called *Cardinal Secrets*. It uncovered complaints within the Archdiocese of Dublin ignored by both police and Church hierarchy. The Ferns, Cloyne, Murphy and Ryan Inquiries were all set in motion, revealing clergy child sexual abuse on a horrific scale and showing that, 'Ireland's police colluded with the Catholic Church in covering up clerical child abuse in Dublin on a huge scale.'

Another documentary, *The Shame of the Catholic Church*, revealed that in 1975 Ireland's most senior cleric, Cardinal Seán Brady, took statements from teenage boys concerning their abuse by Father Brendan Smyth. Brady refused to allow the father of one boy, Brendan Boland, to remain while his son was interviewed. The Cardinal's questions included: 'Did you enjoy it?' and 'Have you ever done this with another man or boy before, if not, why not?'

Fearing others might also be abused, young Boland provided Brady with the names and addresses of other boys and girls Smyth was visiting. He wanted the Church to protect them. Cardinal Brady never told police or warned the parents. No action was ever taken. Smyth continued to abuse children for the best part of two decades, including all those Boland named to Cardinal Brady.

At the end of his interview Brady handed the boy a bible and had him swear an oath. The same procedure used with Denis McAlinden's nieces.

As events unfolded in Ireland and the *Boston Globe* stories broke in the USA, I was about to become immersed in another clergy child sexual abuse investigation back in the Hunter Valley.

CHAPTER 9

GOING OFF THE RAILS

Brother Bernard McGrath was gaoled in 1997 for sexually abusing an eleven-year-old boy at Morisset's Kendall Grange home for disadvantaged boys, forty kilometres south-west of Newcastle. McGrath had already been convicted of child abuse charges relating to the St John of God's (SOG) Marylands Institution for boys in Christchurch, New Zealand. He would face hundreds more charges relating to violently abusing boys at the SOG home in Morisset.

New Zealand Police would later seek extradition of Father Raymond Garchow and Religious Brothers Rodger Moloney and William Lebler, all of whom had associations with Kendall Grange, after further allegations surfaced back at the SOG Christchurch facility.

With McGrath a director at Morisset, his child victims had nowhere to hide from his sadistic abuse. In 2018, Joanne McCarthy would write: 'A terrified eight-year-old boy waited to be raped as another boy's screams could be heard from a nearby room where two St John of God Brothers had taken him.' Other accounts of abuse at the school were just as harrowing.

The same year, a former student of Newcastle's St Pius X High School contacted Broken Rites. In the 1970s his mother complained to Church authorities that Father John Denham had sexually abused her son. Denham was moved. Two decades later, Broken Rites did what the Church should have done and referred the man to police. Convicted in 2000, Denham received a suspended sentence, yet there was no investigation for the earlier concealment of Denham's crimes.

Although aware of these cases, I had no direct involvement. I was, nevertheless, interested. Along with Denis McAlinden and Vince Ryan, these new cases heightened my interest and belief in the need for further scrutiny of the Church.

At that same time, I had my hands full in the detectives' office at Maitland. The Lower Hunter was one of the busiest in the state and was desperately short of police. In addition to managing staff, I also conducted major investigations. When the two other detective sergeants left and weren't replaced for some years, I was left with additional work.

At the beginning of June 2002, I received a phone call from a DPP lawyer. We had known each other professionally, but this time his call wasn't specifically about work. A friend's son had been sexually abused and I was asked if I would speak with him.

The young man was supposed to come to my office on Monday, 3 June, but he didn't show up. Unknown to me he had walked to the front of the police station, but couldn't bring himself to walk through the door. It wasn't an easy step. When we eventually did meet, this young man's story would impact me more than any other crime I had investigated.

•

Daniel Feenan's abuse started in 1988 when he was twelve. It was something he would rather forget.

His real story began years earlier. Back then he'd been happy, without a care in the world, growing up the eldest of four brothers in the farmlands of the Williams River. Life was filled with love, church, family and cricket. As I came to know his family later, I was struck by their closeness. The only thing to ever come between them was cricket. Even as adults, the banter and rivalry between brothers debating each other's cricketing prowess remains undiminished. Friendly jibes among fond memories. A photo hangs in Pat Feenan's home of her boys and their father, all in cricket whites. Happier times.

The family's glue was Patricia, or Pat as she prefers, whom I introduced back in the first chapter at the Newcastle forum. Pat held her family together through trying times, withstanding more than a mother should have to.

John converted to Catholicism some years after marrying Pat. His confirmation alongside Daniel was a proud family moment. Pat and John worked tirelessly, giving both time and money to the Church. Pat was a special minister, prominent on the parish council, church roster and more. John volunteered his accountancy skills before going on to work for the Maitland–Newcastle Diocese as its business manager.

Growing up in the Feenan family was fun and carefree. As the eldest, Daniel was looked up to by his siblings, and other parents admired his politeness and manners. He was a good-looking boy with the world at his feet, excelling both academically and at sport. His parents knew Daniel would achieve whatever he desired in life.

Things changed. Pat and John initially attributed the changes to puberty. Daniel was in Year 10 and school captain at Maitland Marist Brothers when his grades began to drop. Then came the rebellious behaviour, unexplained disappearances and withdrawing to his room. Mothers always notice. Pat saw her son was no longer interested in study; he just sat in his room staring out the window. His thoughts were a mystery. Everyone was locked out and they felt it best to give him space.

As good Catholics, Pat and John sought Father James Fletcher's counsel. Father Jim had been close to the Feenans since arriving in the parish in 1987, encouraging Daniel and his brothers to become altar boys. A regular visitor for meals, afternoon tea and family celebrations, he was almost family. Father Jim's thoughts on Daniel caught Pat by surprise: 'It's that time in his life that Daniel needs some independence. He has always been very close to his family and needs to break away from this.'

Pat baulked at Fletcher's remark.

She and John hoped that when Daniel completed school, things might improve. They didn't. There was no more striving to excel. Aimless and working as a concrete labourer, Daniel spent his afternoons drinking, coming home quarrelsome and often violent. Household items would be smashed, holes punched in walls amid arguments with his family. Daniel was off the rails. No one, not even Pat, knew how to control him. She knew it wasn't normal. Her other boys were fine, but she had no answer for her eldest.

At age nineteen in 1995 Daniel came home drunk, very drunk. He'd stopped taking his anti-depressants and his behaviour was spiralling out of control. Pat was waiting for him. They needed to talk. After he staggered through the door Pat sat him down. Daniel, however, wasn't in a mood to listen. He never was. As he stormed off, Pat sat exasperated, wondering what to do next. She was losing her son and nothing she did seemed to change the situation. Whenever she asked what was going on, Daniel just shut down.

Call it intuition, a mother's instinct, but Pat had an uncomfortable feeling that afternoon. Everything was quiet, too quiet. The interior of the farm shed was dark against the day. She decided to walk down and check. As she arrived, Daniel was on a trailer beside the tractor with a rope over a beam.

'Daniel, don't do this!'

Too late. Daniel had jumped, and the rope jerked his body to an abrupt halt. His legs dangled back and forth above the ground.

Pat screamed with everything her lungs could muster. Her only hope was the neighbours. They were too far away to hear but she continued yelling anyway, screaming hysterically as she ran to her son and wrapped her arms around his legs. Each time Pat lifted, Daniel's legs merely bent. The rope tightened. It cut deeper into the flesh around his neck. Her son's life was literally slipping through her arms. Pat looked desperately around for something to cut the rope. She saw nothing. Even if she did, it was unlikely she could reach high enough.

Pat's screams turned to sobs just as her youngest son appeared. Jumping off the school bus, eleven-year-old Bernard was walking to the house when he heard his mother's cries. Throwing his school bag from his back, he ran.

When I spoke to Bernard years later, his memory of that day was a blur. He remembered his mother's desperation in trying to lift Daniel, the rope around his brother's neck, and the colour draining from Daniel's face. He didn't remember climbing onto the trailer, or how he managed to get the rope from around his brother's neck, but somehow he did. The rope had cut deep. He remembered the skin being rubbed off behind Daniel's ears and how it had cut into his throat. Daniel still bore the scar when I saw him years later.

Daniel experienced things no person – especially a child – should ever experience. Now Bernard had been exposed to something no eleven-year-old should have to see, but he had saved his brother's life. Perhaps this was what inspired Bernard to later embark on a successful medical career.

After the noose was pulled from his neck, Daniel broke down. Looking at his mother's tears all he could say was, 'Sorry.'

They hugged. After some minutes, Bernard walked his brother back to the house. With both her sons safe, Pat collapsed against the tractor wheel, her body heaving as she sobbed uncontrollably.

Years later, the Church would tell Pat that under its Towards Healing protocol she and Bernard were not victims. They couldn't help her. It was a scar she and Bernard would not forget.

Composing herself, Pat walked from the barn to the house. Daniel was on the floor crying outside his room. Pat sat next to him. Her presence was all he needed. Seeing blood on Daniel's wrists where he had cut them before finding the rope, she said nothing. The bleeding had stopped. There weren't many words between mother and son. There didn't need to be. For now, sitting was enough.

Still drunk, all Daniel wanted to do was sleep. John left work the moment Pat called. When the other boys got home the whole family was distraught. Pat thought about calling the family doctor, but rang Father Jim instead. He readily undertook to help Daniel. Fletcher offered his spare room at the presbytery. He would keep an eye on their son and talk to Daniel when he sobered up. He would be safe, Father Jim assured them. Pat and John were appreciative. Daniel was assisted into the car and dozed off as his father drove to the Branxton presbytery.

The following morning, Daniel was in an even darker mood and rang his father to pick him up. Father Jim was unsuccessful in discussing anything. A doctor and psychiatrist fared no better.

Eventually Daniel moved to Nelson Bay in the first of many failed relationships. He remained prone to violent outbursts and his drinking worsened. Late one evening in 1998, Daniel turned up outside the Nelson Bay presbytery yelling obscenities and smashing bottles. Father Bob Searle walked out to calm him. It was no use. Daniel was too worked up. Knowing the family, Searle telephoned Pat. Embarrassed at the time, Pat later realised her son's behaviour was a cry for help.

When Daniel returned to the Feenan family home, nothing changed. His violence escalated to the point of his parents having to call police. Over the next few years he moved interstate, had failed relationships and continued meltdowns.

In November 2000, John and Pat separated. Daniel's ongoing issues were undoubtedly a factor.

On a December night in 2000, Daniel called his mother. He had moved to Tasmania and Pat knew he'd been drinking, which wasn't unusual. For whatever reason, this night, he was happy to talk, and Pat was only too happy to listen. The break-up of his parents affected Daniel deeply. He told her he had been to see a doctor and psychiatrist, which pleased her. Daniel was finally seeking help on his own. There was a long pause before a question jumped unexpectedly into Pat's mind. She didn't mean for it to come out, it just happened.

'Daniel, I want to ask you something and I want you to give me an honest answer. Have you ever been sexually abused?'

A deep breath before Daniel sombrely replied, 'Yes.'

Pat sensed her son's tears over the phone, longing to hold him. At the same time her stomach churned. It wasn't comforting to know he had been abused, but there it was. Finally, an answer. All the pieces began falling into place. An explanation for his falling off the rails, the drinking, the violent outbursts and failed relationships. There were many unanswered questions, but they would have to wait. Daniel wasn't up to explaining, not yet, not over the phone. He would fly home. For now, that was enough.

Pat spoke to John before confiding in their other sons. When Daniel flew home he backed away from discussing what had happened. Pat was disappointed, but accepted he wasn't ready. His brothers weren't as patient. They suggested a night on the town. It had been a while since they'd all been together. Besides, a few drinks might free up the conversation. Anyway, that was the plan.

Pat remembered four young men pouring out of a taxi on the front lawn at two in the morning. It was then his brothers managed to get Daniel to divulge a little more. He'd been raped by Father Jim. Daniel erupted into a violent rage and would say no more. It took some time for Daniel's brothers to settle him. But Pat's night wasn't yet over. Her middle sons, Luke and Dominic, were threatening to drive to the Branxton presbytery with a couple of house bricks. Not to throw through the window, but to slam together over a certain part of Fletcher's anatomy. Pat confiscated their car keys and managed to get them all into bed before sitting bolt upright, listening for any sound they might try to leave and carry out their threat.

Daniel returned to Tasmania before moving once more. Pat encouraged him to talk, but to no avail. He had said all he was going to say for the time being. She decided against approaching the Church or Fletcher until Daniel was ready.

In 2001 Pat got a call from a Brisbane hospital. Daniel had again attempted suicide. This time he'd thrown himself in front of an oncoming car. Admitted to the psychiatric ward of a Brisbane hospital, he was placed on medication. John and Pat travelled to his bedside. To Pat's relief, Daniel agreed to return to the family home.

Now aged twenty-four, Daniel met Donna in mid-2001. Gentle as she was pretty, Donna was the first partner in whom Daniel confided. Donna lent her support and promised to stand by Daniel, no matter what. It wasn't long before they were expecting a baby. Daniel told his mother he had finally settled down. That was all well and good, but Pat had heard it before. He would do well for a time before the slightest thing would set him off. Daniel explained that those moments came from memories he couldn't control. Maybe so, but Pat had had enough. Over time, to prove he had changed, Daniel slowly opened up through tears and many hugs.

•

Fletcher last raped Daniel the night he attempted to hang himself. The night Pat and John unknowingly delivered Daniel into the arms of the devil. Daniel was still intoxicated as Fletcher plied him with paracetamol and more alcohol. The following morning Daniel discovered evidence Fletcher had raped him while he lay unconscious. In a rage, Daniel threatened to kill the priest. Finding his phone, Daniel called his father to pick him up. Pat now understood why Daniel returned in a dark mood.

Although Daniel revealed more, he couldn't go into detail. Pat reassured him nothing could alter her love. Even so, Daniel felt ashamed and embarrassed. He knew he had been the victim, but still it didn't change him feeling 'dirty and horrible'.

Many survivors have told me the same.

Pat reminded Daniel he was about to become a father. His abuse couldn't rule his life, adding they were 'sick to death of his long miserable journey of self-destruction'.

Pat wanted to know what he was going to do to turn his life around. She didn't expect his answer: 'I've been thinking of going to the police.'

Pat felt an overwhelming sense of relief. After talking with John, she called her friend at the DPP, who in turn called me.

CHAPTER 10

WALKING THROUGH THE DOOR

Daniel folded his arms against the cold, his gaze fixed on the doors of the police station opposite. Watching people come and go, he kept telling himself that all he had to do was walk through those doors. Easier said than done. He'd tried a couple of times, but his feet seemed nailed to the pavement. Leaning against the warmth of the fire station's brick wall opposite the police station, he hoped it would somehow push him across the road. It didn't. After what seemed an eternity, Daniel finally made a decision.

After telling his family he would speak to police, Daniel walked away. I didn't see Daniel that cold June morning in 2002. The night before, something else had happened. The *60 Minutes* television program aired 'Loss of Faith'. Reporter Richard Carlton interviewed Archbishop George Pell about his knowledge of notorious paedophile priest Gerald Ridsdale. In particular, the abuse of Ridsdale's nephew. It was a brilliant interview and caused a sensation.

As Daniel's mother watched the program, she hoped Daniel wouldn't be doing the same. As fate would have it, he was. It wasn't so much the controversy surrounding Pell; for Daniel it was about other victims. Daniel had never given much thought to others. The more he heard, the more tears came to his eyes. Then everything exploded. Donna was frightened as Daniel stood in their living room yelling at the television. The realisation he wasn't the first to have been abused by a priest registered. Frantically looking through the phone book, he finally found what he was looking for and called the church presbytery at Branxton.

Daniel unleashed a torrent of verbal abuse. The rage within him released. When Fletcher eventually got a chance he asked, 'Who is this?'

Daniel replied, 'You know.'

Describing what Fletcher did to him, raped him time and again, Daniel's words were not subtle. His language matched his anger. He didn't need to say who he was, or so he thought – how could Fletcher forget? Daniel was his favourite, the one he had singled out for praise and special gifts. He bloody well knew, all right. Most people would have hung up, but not Fletcher; instead he stayed on the other end, listening. Truth was, Fletcher really didn't know who was calling. Daniel wasn't his only victim. There were others. That's why he didn't hang up. He listened, trying to figure out which boy it was. The anger in Daniel's voice was such that Fletcher couldn't identify him, leaving the priest in a quandary.

I had been a detective a long time, sometimes I thought too long. When Daniel didn't show up, I guessed the reason. I'd watched *60 Minutes* too. Looking at the clock and my notes, I decided to ring. It was the first time we spoke. Daniel explained his not turning up and being unable to walk into the station. I understood. What I didn't know about until then, was his call to Fletcher.

During our conversation Daniel and I hit it off. The longer we spoke, the more at ease he became.

'I'm not that scary,' I assured him. 'How about we give it another try?'

This time, I would wait for him outside the station.

When Daniel turned up, he tried to appear calm. In reality, he looked anything but as he clung to Donna. We shook hands and talked for a few minutes. He still wasn't keen to go through those doors.

'Today we won't be doing anything but talking,' I assured him.

Daniel just nodded. We walked through the doors together. It was the start of a long journey I would walk with him.

I led Daniel and Donna past Maitland Police Station's front counter, up the stairs and into the quieter surrounds of my office. Wide-eyed, they examined the unfamiliar surroundings as I showed them to the seats opposite my desk. Trays, pens and various files surrounded my computer. Scattered about were pieces of paper with coffee-cup stains amid notes I had scribbled in haste. On my wall hung a sign: *A Clean Desk is the Sign of a Sick Mind.*

It's not that I didn't like a tidy desk, it's just how I worked. The cleaner and I had an agreement. 'Just clean around the edges.'

A mess it may have been, but I knew exactly where everything was.

'Can I get you a coffee?'

Daniel and Donna stared blankly.

'I've been hanging out for one myself and it's no extra trouble,' I assured them. I'd only just had one, but I wanted to put them at ease.

Coffee and a walk with Daniel while he had a smoke became our routine. A decade and a half later, I laugh to myself remembering Daniel had two sugars and milk. Funny how little things stick. Eventually Daniel deputised himself. I'd be busy typing when Daniel would just say, 'Coffee?' before heading out to make us both a cup. The coffee wasn't good – just the cheap variety the social club provided, served in elegant white styrofoam – but at two dollars a pay, I couldn't complain.

I could see Daniel had a thousand questions that first day. *Will I have to go to court? Will I have to hire a lawyer? How long will this take?*

I'd heard them all before and answered as many as I could. Many questions were prefaced, *Will I have to …*

That wasn't unusual. Now Daniel had walked into a police station he feared he would be railroaded into a process over which he had no control. I had a clarification, a spiel if you like.

'Firstly, if you don't want this matter to go any further you can walk out of here today without repercussions. Nothing further will happen. It's up to you.

'Secondly, I can make an official record and give you the report number. If you don't want me to do anything further, that's fine. It's your decision.

'Thirdly, you can make a statement and I'll give you a copy. That doesn't mean you have to go to court. If you want more time to think, even years, your statement will be on file and your case can be investigated later. Again, it's your decision.

'Finally, you can have it investigated and depending on the outcome, you might have to go to court. Regardless of what you decide, it will be your decision. No one is going to force you to do anything you don't want.'

I liked to use an analogy of driving a car. Daniel was in the driver's seat. He could start the car and steer wherever he wanted. He could hit the accelerator to go forward, or the brake to stop. If he didn't like where he was going, all he had to do was step on the brake, get out and walk away. He was the one in control.

Why the emphasis on all decisions being his, and on him being in control? Survivors were abused in a power imbalance. The offender commits these crimes for their own gratification, but underlying is an abuse of power. It makes the offender – the adult – feel strong. For the child, it is the exact opposite. They are vulnerable, powerless, a feeling that accompanies most into adulthood. That's why many never disclose what happened. Saying to Daniel, *It's your decision,* put him in the driver's seat. He was now in control, the one with the power.

As we talked, I assessed the young man opposite. Daniel was smart, very smart. Despite the disruption to his schooling he had a good education, was articulate and had manners to boot. It didn't take me long to work out that if he went to court, we stood a better chance than most. Many survivors of childhood sexual abuse didn't have Daniel's advantages. From lower socio-economic backgrounds, lacking education or from dysfunctional homes, many never have a chance. It was for those reasons they were targeted in the first place. Perpetrators exploit vulnerabilities knowing there is little chance of a complaint, and if there is, the survivor is unlikely to be believed. If a charge ever made it to court, a smart barrister would tear the survivor apart in the witness box. I later heard a Supreme Court judge say, 'Having had thirty or forty years of experience with child sexual assault cases, I don't think I'd ever advocate for my children to go through the process.'

Daniel sat learning forward. We must have talked for an hour that first day when he asked, 'Do I have to do a statement today?'

'Not if you don't want to.'

Daniel finally leaned back. It had been worrying him. I was annoyed I hadn't picked up on it earlier. Although I told Daniel outside I had no plans to start typing, not everything had registered. I wanted to give him time for everything to sink in. That said, he insisted on making an official record of his abuse before leaving. And that's what happened, no more, no less. We didn't go into detail, just a brief overview. The rest could wait. He left feeling something had begun.

As he got up to go, I asked Daniel who knew he was coming to the police station. He told me, 'No one.'

Except his family and the friend at the DPP. I asked him to keep it that way.

'And no more angry phone calls.'

I didn't want Fletcher finding out before I had a chance to confront him. Daniel assured me he would say nothing. Knowing he would have more questions, I handed him my card. 'Ring me anytime.'

Over the next week I checked the police system to see if Fletcher reported Daniel's abusive call. He didn't. Police can trace calls, it isn't hard, but Fletcher chose not to report it. Why? The caller had angrily alleged Fletcher sexually abused him. It's pretty serious stuff. If there was no truth to the allegation, I asked myself, why not report it?

•

I had a block of days off when I got a call from the station saying Pat Feenan wanted to speak with me. When I called her back, she apologised profusely for interrupting my time off.

'Don't worry,' I told her, 'it happens all the time. It comes with the job.'

Pat had news, and it wasn't good. Her estranged husband, John, had a good relationship with his boss, Bishop Michael Malone. John was also a good Catholic. Having separated from Pat, and with his family going through an upheaval, he had to talk to someone. So, he opened up to Malone about his son's abuse.

Pat learned about their conversation when Malone called to offer her his support. She was shocked John had spoken to someone outside the family, let alone someone in the Church. It was too late. If this wasn't bad enough, Malone then told Pat he'd been to Branxton. Pat recoiled, dreading what she was about to hear. Fletcher still hadn't known the abusive caller's identity – that is, until Malone told him. Pat was annoyed with John and angry with the Bishop, but bit her tongue to glean more. Malone said he confronted Fletcher about Daniel's allegation and Fletcher denied it. The thing was, Malone hadn't known the details, no one did. Why confront someone without all the information? It was then Malone dropped the real bombshell: he told Fletcher about Daniel going to see the police. Fletcher now knew he was under investigation. The element of surprise was gone. Without time to prepare, offenders often blurt something out without thinking, or give inconsistent answers. Maybe Fletcher wouldn't have done that but, after Malone's visit, I would never know.

Pat's anger rose until she could bite her tongue no longer. Infuriated, she asked Malone why he'd gone anywhere near Fletcher. His answer: 'To offer pastoral support to a fellow priest.'

Pat could only interpret the visit in different terms: a tip-off.

Malone didn't speak to Fletcher alone, it was more like a council of priests. Monsignor Jim Saunders and Father Bill Burston were there, with Father Des Harrigan arriving soon after. Great, thought Pat, now the whole bloody Diocese knows.

I don't know who was the more ropable, Pat or myself. That said, John would have expected what occurred between the Bishop and himself to remain confidential. For decades the Church had refused to report child sexual abuse, arguing such knowledge came about in confidence. On this occasion, that confidence seemingly didn't extend to John ... or Daniel.

Over the years, Pat told me, Fletcher had shown John and Pat inappropriate literature, cartoon drawings of sex acts and the like, which could have assisted the investigation. No doubt, thanks to his opportune warning, Fletcher would have disposed of anything incriminating.

Pat had devoted herself to the Church her entire life, yet, not surprisingly, I sensed her wariness toward some clergy. From here on, I decided to exercise greater caution.

●

Being a cop in a country town isn't always easy. Sometimes a police officer's work and his own life cross paths. At Cessnock I played rugby union alongside teammates I had arrested. I saw it as black and white. When I was at work, I was at work. There was no fear or favour. I still got along with everyone within the team; I just kept my job separate from my social life.

It was a similar story where I lived in Branxton. I was aware Jim Fletcher was the local priest, I had seen him on a few occasions but didn't really know him. Our neighbours and good friends, Steve and Lisa, had been married by Fletcher. That's just country towns. Around this time I learned Fletcher was continuing to visit the Church's local primary school. Like

Denis McAlinden, he enjoyed the excitement of pulling lollies out of his pockets for the kids. How did I know? Because our eleven-year-old daughter was a student there. Speaking to colleagues, all agreed I had no power to stop him, not until I could arrest him and impose bail conditions.

As a police officer I could do no more. As a parent, however, I could. We sat our daughter down to a difficult conversation. How do you tell a child these sorts of things? We didn't tell her why, but we made it absolutely clear she was to have nothing to do with Father Jim. We put various other measures in place to ensure she went nowhere near him. We shouldn't have had to address this considering the Church and school principal knew of Daniel's allegations. Fletcher's continued access to children was reprehensible. I had been able to safeguard our daughter, but what about others? I knew many parents through the school, junior netball and being a retained firefighter. Whether I knew them or not was beside the point; I felt compelled to do more.

I might have been overstepping the mark, but I decided to have a word with Bishop Malone. As I walked into Newcastle's Sacred Heart Cathedral, its grandeur failed to impress me. My mind was on other matters. Led to an upstairs room, my colleague and I met with Bishop Malone and his Vicar General, Monsignor Jim Saunders. I got straight to the point, telling them I was investigating serious allegations of child sexual abuse. When I asked Malone if there had been prior concerns about Fletcher, he replied, 'No, not before John Feenan approached me'.

As for Malone meeting Fletcher: 'Did you tell him that the matter had been reported to the police and there was an investigation?'

Malone conceded. 'Yes. This was only done because of our concern for his welfare.'

By putting an allegation to Fletcher, Malone effectively started his own investigation, despite Towards Healing stating, 'No Church investigation shall be undertaken in such a manner as to interfere in any way with the proper processes of criminal or civil law.'

Malone telling Fletcher that Daniel had been to the police jeopardised my investigation, and I told him so.

Saunders interjected, 'We were concerned about the police arriving on his doorstep and taking him without anyone knowing.'

Annoyed, I said, 'We are not like the Gestapo, arriving in the middle of the night and dragging him off to a cell somewhere.'

I told them it remained my intention to notify the Church before Fletcher was arrested. Saunders, in his best white cassock, leapt to his feet, thrust his arms toward the ceiling before bringing his hands down together in prayer. The Church praying for Fletcher, but what about the kids?

Turning to Malone, I said, 'In your conversation, was Father Fletcher aware of a police investigation before you raised the subject with him?'

I already knew the answer.

'No. I don't believe so.'

'In view of that, would it not have been wiser to not mention the investigation to him?'

'Sorry?'

I made it clearer. 'If you had not told him there was a police investigation he may not have been upset or distressed and therefore, negate any need for concern over his welfare in the first place?'

'I see what you mean.' Malone then reverted back to, 'I did not mean for that to occur, our concern was for his welfare.'

Exasperated, I told him, 'If someone like Richard Carleton was to interview you, I doubt that he would be as accepting of that explanation. It could be suggested that the purpose of your visit had the effect of warning Father Fletcher.'

Malone denied that was his purpose. Intended or not, the outcome was the same. Before leaving I asked for Fletcher to be kept away from children.

Malone's question left me dismayed. 'Do you have any concerns for other persons?'

Yes, I did. The allegations were serious and related to when Fletcher picked up Daniel as a child from school. Anthony and Chrissie Foster's children were abused at school. I reminded him of Vince Ryan targeting boys at school.

'I know Father Fletcher is still in the Branxton Parish and, as such, has contact with the Catholic school there and probably other children's groups. I would feel better if he was removed from the parish and placed into an office role here.'

'You're saying you feel he should be relieved of his position?'

Without hesitation I confirmed. 'I would. I cannot force you to do that. I don't have that power, but I would strongly suggest it to you.'

Malone countered, 'There is a presumption of innocence until proven guilty.'

Agreeing, I reminded him of his duty of care. The protection of children had to come first. I had charged a police officer and schoolteachers with sexual offences in the past – in each case, I told him, the person was removed.

'I can only ask you to consider doing the same.'

I left with the impression he would do the right thing but whatever steps he took were ineffective as Fletcher remained in his parish.

Patrick Parkinson, a law professor, had reviewed Towards Healing two years earlier. Citing the High Court, Parkinson explained that children were vulnerable and needed special protection. He suggested moving priests to administrative roles whenever there was potential danger to children.

'... the unacceptable risk test is a moral principle as well as a legal one.' And 'No one should be permitted to exercise a public ministry if doing so presents an unacceptable risk of abuse to children or young people.'

Parkinson's recommendation had been incorporated into Towards Healing. Despite this, Fletcher remained where he was.

•

Despite Fletcher claiming to be in poor health, the Diocese announced it was expanding Fletcher's parish. It would now incorporate neighbouring Lochinvar with its schools adjacent to Fletcher's new presbytery. I wondered if the Church was trying to tell me something.

When Pat heard the announcement, she was furious. As a parent and schoolteacher she knew the danger of leaving Fletcher anywhere near children. Calling Branxton's St Brigid's Primary School, she was told Father Jim visited regularly and was popular with the kids. He even tutored children's reading classes.

Alarmed at Fletcher's continued access to children, Pat contacted the Catholic Church's Professional Standards Office and spoke to its director, John Daveron, who in turn rang me. Echoing Pat's apprehensions, I told him of my meeting with Malone, saying Fletcher should be removed. Fletcher stayed where he was.

Officially, as a police officer, I could do nothing. As a parent, I could not do nothing.

I hadn't previously paid any attention to Fletcher when visiting my daughter's school. I wasn't a Catholic, so Fletcher didn't notice me. That now changed. On parenting visits, Fletcher glanced in my direction, acutely aware of my presence. Someone had obviously said something. I didn't mind. In fact, I went out of my way to make sure he noticed me keeping an eye on him. If looking over his shoulder kept a kid safe, it paid off.

Towards the end of 2002, our second son graduated from St Peter's Campus in Maitland, the same school Daniel had attended, but now renamed. You can imagine my disgust when Fletcher walked on stage to present crucifixes to the students. Our son threw his away.

•

I made the odd call to see how Daniel was going. I didn't broach his statement, leaving it to him to say if and when he was ready. I mostly checked on Daniel through Pat. I didn't want Daniel feeling badgered.

It didn't take long for Malone's visit to Fletcher to reap ugly rewards. I soon became aware that Fletcher was poisoning parishioners against the Feenans. He portrayed Daniel as a drunkard and no-hoper. Fletcher didn't hesitate to use confidential knowledge of Daniel's suicide attempt to discredit his victim. Who would the faithful believe, a disturbed young man or a man of God?

Many took up Fletcher's banner, seeing the accusations against their priest as an attack on their Church. Denunciations were nasty as ostracism propelled malicious whispers. Pat felt her cherished Church turning against her. Two thousand years ago another mother stood by her son as he was nailed to a cross. Pat did the same.

•

I was kept busy while waiting for Daniel. Unlike in television shows, police don't look after just one case at a time. Actively working on two murder investigations, I was preparing a third for trial when contacted by Annette, the McAlinden abuse survivor who first contacted Mark Watters three years earlier in 1999. Mark had been promoted to a uniform position on the Central Coast, so I spoke with Annette. She told me of hearing a rumour. Bishop Clarke was supposed to have spoken with two women who were also victims of McAlinden. Annette had no idea who they were, and asked me if I could approach Clarke.

I found Emeritus Bishop Leo Clarke residing at a Catholic Retirement Village near Lake Macquarie, where he told me he knew nothing about McAlinden's victims. Asking where McAlinden might now be, Clarke deflected. 'You'd have to speak to Bishop Malone, I'm afraid. I cannot help you.'

Perhaps I should have pushed harder, asked more questions, but I had nothing more than a rumour to act on. Telephoning the Diocese, I fared no better. Annette was disappointed, but appreciated my asking. That done, I now swung my attention back to the Fletcher investigation.

CHAPTER 11

THE SOUL'S DARKEST SECRETS

In November 2002, Daniel had made up his mind. He wanted to go to court.

'Okay,' I said. 'Let's get started.'

Daniel didn't want anyone hearing the details – not Donna, not his mother, no one. It was just him and me. He felt embarrassed, despite my assurances. This was going to be tough, not just for Daniel, but for both of us.

In decades of being a detective I had seen awful things and listened to terrible stories. None prepared me for what I was about to hear. Daniel detailed his childhood, and the way the priest ingrained himself in the Feenan family. Nothing too hard to start with. I wanted him to get used to the process before we tackled the more confronting aspects.

A police officer's job is to listen, sort out what's relevant and admissible, then type it down chronologically in the victim's own words. I liked to angle my computer screen so my interviewee could read and correct as we went. Like anything, the more statements you type, the more proficient you become. By this point, I had done my fair share.

Some police electronically recorded statements then sent the disc away to be transcribed. This was lazy policing as far as I was concerned. Instead of a flowing narrative, prosecutors were left trying to interpret a jumble of questions and answers. When something was omitted you couldn't go back and put it in the relevant passage. To understand how it related, readers had to flick back through a transcript to find the connection. The DPP discouraged the practice and I agreed.

As Daniel began, past issues surfaced. Despite counselling and psychological help, he swung between periods of depression and stress, mingled with outbursts of anger. It didn't bother me, I understood. Alcohol was Daniel's escape, leaving his family with the fallout. He was hospitalised after again becoming suicidal. Everything ground to a halt. It was a tremendous drain, but not one of his family withheld their support.

Pat kept me apprised as Daniel's health fluctuated. I began wondering about the merits of continuing as I visited him in the mental health unit at Maitland Hospital.

Looking up, Daniel appeared drained, his eyes red. Seeing me he sat up. 'What are you doing here?'

I wasn't wearing work attire. It was my day off, so my wife, Penny, had dropped me on her way into town.

'Given a choice between shopping and discussing the current Ashes tour, I'll take discussing cricket with you any day.'

At least I got Daniel to smile. We did talk cricket, but first I had to get other things out of the way.

Daniel knew his family were worried. I was too. Reliving everything through his statement wasn't easy. I wanted him to know he didn't have to continue. He could still hit the brakes, get out and walk away. He was letting no one down, least of all me. Daniel listened before saying he really wanted to finish his statement. He needed to, not for me, not for his family, but for himself. He wanted to deal with the demons and his soul's darkest secrets. I just didn't want him thinking he was being pushed. I told Daniel to spend time with his family and watch some cricket over Christmas. His statement could wait.

I continued visiting Daniel as he struggled to stay out of hospital. Pat and I met for the first time when we visited together. While Daniel fought his past, Pat dealt with the present. She hadn't told him of the Bishop's betrayal. We knew Daniel had enough problems.

Maitland is a tight-knit community with a grapevine second to none. Through it, Pat heard that Fletcher and his supporters were taking a perverted delight in Daniel's struggles. Alcohol abuse, mental breakdowns and suicide attempts were all used to discredit him. No one asked why a promising young man from a good family had so many issues. The Church had done such a good job of covering up and silencing abuse survivors it left most parishioners blinded to the ongoing effects of that abuse. Acknowledging its crimes and apologies weren't yet fully in the Church's repertoire.

Condemnation wasn't just reserved for Daniel; his entire family bore the brunt. Pat received menacing late-night phone calls, while John endured glaring looks and whispers at work. One of Daniel's brothers became involved in a fight defending his older sibling's reputation. In another disgusting episode, a local parishioner rammed Pat with a shopping trolley in a supermarket. I urged Pat to make a complaint, but she declined, saying it would only distract from Daniel's investigation. Around this time Pat collapsed at work from all the stress and had to be hospitalised.

Donna turned everything around when their son arrived just before Christmas. Daniel was elated. When Pat called with the news I heard the joy in her voice. This baby was just the tonic they needed. Daniel took my advice, spending time with family and watching cricket. I was happy for him to take all the time he needed.

•

I have wrestled with how much I would say about Fletcher's crimes in the pages of this book. The eye so easily sweeps past the words *child sexual abuse* without really understanding what it means. Some don't want to know. The physical pain, horror, trauma, fear, depravity and utter betrayal. I would like to tell you. I want you to understand because for so long it was overlooked. I want others to know why a Child Abuse Royal Commission was needed. But how can I do that?

Even with delicate words and sensitivity, it would still numb. In my career, I witnessed and heard the most terrible of crimes, and yet Daniel's story traumatised me. It still does. So, with Daniel's consent I have tried to find a balance. Even so, I can only convey a small part of what happened. Just know the full story was much, much worse.

It had been three months since we last worked on Daniel's statement. By mid-February 2003, he was again ready. About to get into the heavier material, I wanted to spend as much time with Daniel as possible, so I organised not to be disturbed. As it turned out, we spent the entire day together, and then some. There were tears as the past crept back. At times Daniel struggled to get the words out. Plenty of breaks, many walks, and a regular supply of coffee.

Daniel told me about Fletcher's contrasting behaviour. How, as a boy, he was both shocked and delighted when Fletcher told crude jokes using the F and C words. Their talks became personal. Daniel didn't understand he was being groomed.

As a ten-year-old, it was all captivating and flattering. He was being treated like a grown-up. After the Clarence Town Church service, Fletcher would tell Daniel's parents he needed an extra altar boy for his Dungog service. In reality, it was an excuse for them to be alone. On those trips they would talk about, well, men's stuff. Fletcher didn't use the word *secret*, telling Daniel, 'This is our special time.'

Daniel came to understand that these conversations were never to leave the priest's car.

When Fletcher began driving Daniel home from St Peters' Campus in Maitland, Pat and John appreciated the help. After all, with their own careers, school, sport and everything else, they had three other boys to run around. When Luke, the second eldest, joined Daniel at St Peters, Fletcher had to be more cunning. He worked out the days Daniel stayed back for sport or school cadets.

During one ordinary afternoon drive home, Fletcher diverted from their usual route, driving to Walka Water Works, an historic feature then set in bushland just outside Maitland.

After the crime of subjecting his victim to oral sex, Fletcher told Daniel, 'There's nothing wrong with this … It's normal and it's a natural part of life. A lot of people do it, but it is to just stay between you and me. No one else should know about this, it is our secret. You won't mention this to your parents or anyone else, will you?'

Daniel nodded as Fletcher assured, 'You know, your father probably did exactly the same thing and he still keeps it a secret.'

Daniel knew priests never lied, therefore, it must be true. All the way home Fletcher kept reassuring the boy what they had done was normal. Like the crude jokes and other conversations, everything was to stay between them.

Fletcher would walk into the school playground making a fuss over his favourite altar boy. Simple, but it worked. Daniel saw the other boys envious of the attention he was receiving. It made him feel important.

The frequency of offences continued to increase. Daniel didn't enjoy what was happening. Far from it. By this time, however, it was routine. He did whatever he was told as Fletcher reinforced, 'This is our special time.' There were other places Fletcher drove to, mostly isolated rural settings, parks and roadside clearings.

One afternoon Fletcher didn't turn down the usual road. Instead they made their way through a tranquil park dotted with poplar trees on the edge of the picturesque village of Paterson. Perched high on the western bank of the Paterson River, the park was popular on weekends and all but abandoned through the week. That was why it was chosen. There, Daniel was anally raped. In pain, all the young boy could do was focus on the Saint Christopher medal hanging from Fletcher's rear-vision mirror. Daniel watched as it swung back and forth with each of the priest's thrusts. When Fletcher finished, Daniel just lay there, crying, sobbing in pain. The little boy's hurt was such he couldn't move. The exertions took it out of Fletcher. Panting, he looked down at the half-naked child and said, 'Well done.'

Tears streamed from Daniel's eyes as he fixed his school uniform. Fletcher ignored Daniel's whimpering, lighting up a cigarette to savour the moment.

As his pain persisted on the drive home, Daniel noticed Fletcher was worried. The child's discomfort wasn't going away anytime soon. There was a chance someone – most likely Daniel's mother – would ask him what was wrong. He couldn't know what the boy might say. That's when the relationship changed. Instead of coercing Daniel's silence, Fletcher threatened.

'If anyone finds out about this, I am a priest. Everyone knows that priests don't lie. They won't believe you. Remember, you have three brothers, and if you tell anyone I could hurt them too.'

The threats changed everything. Daniel started to understand that what Fletcher was doing was wrong. He also saw the priest's fear. Daniel told me that back then, despite everything that was happening, he still confusingly loved Father Jim.

At home, Daniel wanted to be alone. Bleeding, he said nothing to anyone. As the evening wore on his pain didn't subside. He wanted to ask his mother to take him to a doctor, but couldn't. He had to remain silent to protect his brothers. That night Daniel lay in pain with tears running down his face.

The following morning the bleeding had mostly subsided. Daniel changed his underpants, hiding the bloodstained pair in the bottom of his school bag. He disposed of them later in an industrial bin near his school.

•

At the police station, Daniel sat in front of me remembering what happened. So vivid, the tears again streamed down his face. I nearly cried with him. Daniel was reliving that little boy's pain right in front of me, and it hurt.

It had been a long day working on Daniel's statement. Before he left, I made sure he was in contact with his counsellor.

When I got home, I hugged my kids.

Daniel's family were anxious. They hoped that after so long spent at the police station, everything would be over. Truth was, we still had some way to go. They weren't to know the complexity or gravity of what we were working through.

That weekend Pat sat with her son, comforting and trying to understand what he was enduring. Daniel tried to tell her, but the words dissolved before he could get them out. All he could say was, 'The Saint Christopher medal'.

If only that medal could talk. Daniel couldn't say any more. He didn't need to, the look on his face said it for him. Pat remembered the medal too. She didn't know exactly what happened in Fletcher's car, but she knew that medal had witnessed evil.

Two more days the following week and we were still going. My assessment of Daniel proved correct. He articulated what others struggled to put into words. He recalled the little details, things others forgot. I knew they would prove important, so I spent time recording everything. Fletcher smoking, walking into a shop to buy a can of Coke, odd comments. They would prove crucial.

After the rape at Paterson, Fletcher distanced himself from Daniel's family. The reprieve didn't last long, however, as Fletcher's sexual urges overrode his caution. Pretences fell by the wayside as he continued to make threats. In my office Daniel explained fearing and loving Fletcher at the same time, unable to make sense of his conflicting emotions. What never changed was the abuse. Fletcher committed his crimes with monotonous regularity. Daniel felt like a zombie, doing whatever he was told.

Towards the end of 1990, Fletcher drove Daniel to St Pius X High School at Adamstown, where he raped Daniel in his car just outside the school fence. Looking back, Daniel felt Fletcher's choice of location was risky and the act brazen. Those factors seemed to exacerbate Fletcher's excitement. Why travel forty kilometres from his parish to this school? In later years the school would be exposed as a hot bed of depravity where more than one priest was sexually abusing children.

Around the age of fourteen, Daniel started questioning his relationship with Fletcher as he realised he was attracted to girls. He struggled with his sexuality. His behaviour became erratic as his school grades continued to drop. Daniel felt embarrassed and ashamed, and he hated himself. His affection for Fletcher gradually faded, replaced by loathing. At the age of fifteen, Daniel thought himself old enough. Next time Fletcher tried something, he would put a stop to it.

When Fletcher drove to his favourite secret location at Walka Water Works, Daniel told him, 'It's finished. I am not doing this anymore.'

Taken aback, Fletcher queried, 'What's wrong? Don't you have any feelings for me anymore?'

Daniel fired back, 'No.'

Fletcher became angry, his manner threatening. 'Well, you better think about your brothers. You don't want to see them getting hurt, do you?'

Daniel was prepared and let Fletcher have it. 'If you try anything with them I will run straight to the police. I will tell my parents or anyone that will listen.'

Fletcher retorted, 'They won't believe you. I will tell them you are lying. I told you they will believe a priest any day before they believe you.'

Older and more confident, Daniel called the priest's bluff. He remembered Fletcher's fear that day at Paterson. 'I don't care. I'll take that chance. If I do say something, they'll still be suspicious of you even if they say they believe you.'

Fletcher knew Daniel was right. Dread was written across the priest's face as the conversation became a yelling match.

Breaking down, Daniel shouted, 'If I say something, just try to touch my brothers. Everyone will still be watching you. There might not be anything to prove what I tell them but they will always be suspicious of you. They will watch you too carefully for you to do anything. I will keep my mouth shut if you want. No one will find out, ever. It will be our secret, but I am not doing this anymore. I have had enough. I don't want anything to do with you ever again.'

It was an uncomfortable drive back to school. Fletcher seethed, not a word being said. Daniel knew that, at last, it was over.

•

Daniel was relieved when we finally put that part of his statement behind us. Hundreds of offences, one blurring into the next. I particularised close to seventy counts of child rape. Now, the grim task of working out which ones were strong enough for court.

We spent hours recording the victim impact on Daniel. How he blamed his family before realising that they too were victims. Relationships with his brothers eroded as he spiralled out of control. Reliance on alcohol and experimentation with drugs made matters worse. Then came the drunken accidents and driving episodes, followed by suicide attempts. Daniel told me he wanted to die the day he jumped from the trailer. Because of Fletcher, he had put his family through hell.

Daniel's health deteriorated and he was hospitalised once more. It called for renewed visits, reassurance and more time.

With the factual parts of Daniel's story behind us, I started speaking with his family. Pat was first. Like Daniel, she had a remarkable memory, in many ways surpassing that of her son.

The little things in Daniel's statement now paid off. Fletcher's odd behaviour, comments, missing pieces of the puzzle started to find a niche. Pat recalled the night her son inexplicably went missing, a school uniform she couldn't find. She wasn't to know they'd been lost in Fletcher's car. Pat recalled Fletcher's inappropriate cartoons, images of penises and the like.

John Daveron became a regular caller on behalf of the Church, wanting to know how my investigation was progressing. The Church wanted to ensure Fletcher was supported when the time came. I didn't say much.

When I mentioned Daveron's name, John Feenan became serious. 'I shouldn't be telling you this, Peter, it might get me into trouble, but do you know Daveron's office is supposed to tell the Ombudsman when it's alleged a priest interfered with a child?'

I had no idea. John explained, 'Well, they are. They have to report it.'

I asked, 'How do you know they didn't?'

'If they did, Fletcher would have been stood down long ago. If you make a call, I'll bet you'll find the Church hasn't done what it should have.'

John knew what he was talking about, and I appreciated the heads-up.

Contacting the Ombudsman proved John right. The Church hadn't said a word about Fletcher. A flurry of phone calls followed with the Ombudsman interested in my meeting with Bishop Malone as they initiated an investigation. The Church was finally forced to remove Fletcher.

When Daniel's health improved, we finalised his victim-impact statement. The last thing was to photograph the locations where Fletcher committed his crimes. Pat and John came to the station that day. I remember John breaking down in tears, consoled by Pat, the enormity hitting him all at once. Their marriage, joy, trust in the Church, and Daniel's innocence all stolen. Before we left, John and Pat met Daniel's counsellor. I'd asked she accompany us as we photographed where Daniel's abuse happened. Daniel's distress was obvious as he pointed out Walka Water Works, Paterson Park and other locations. Daniel signed his statement, close to fifty pages. It had taken months, but was worth the effort. I handed Daniel his copy.

'Finally, all that shit is out of my head and in here,' he said.

Daniel couldn't show his statement to anyone until after the legal process, but he knew its value. Realising he would never be able to tell his story, he said, 'If anyone asks, I can just say, read this.'

Daniel's burden lightened that day. His soul's dark secrets had moved out into the light.

Before we finished, Daniel wanted something added. Strictly speaking, it wasn't evidence. He couldn't say it in court, but he wanted it recorded. He had learned of other boys he knew from school who had been sexually abused by Vince Ryan and other clergy.

'I believe that a lot of those assaults involved young boys like myself in the Cessnock and Maitland areas ... I believed in my mind that it was rampant and I suspected then as I do now that there are networks of priests involved in child abuse and paedophilia. I know that I no longer trust any member of the Catholic Church. If they are not involved in this abuse, they will do anything to cover it up and keep you silent.'

Daniel's words were the catalyst for my next phone call. Troy Grant had been a young uniformed officer at Kurri Kurri. He spent some time in my detective office in Cessnock before I supported him moving to the Crime Squad in Newcastle, where he investigated Vince Ryan.

Now at Dubbo, Troy appreciated me calling about Daniel's comment. He volunteered similar concerns, without me asking. Troy was still incensed at the DPP quashing his application to charge Monsignor Cotter with covering up Vince Ryan's crimes. His investigation started with a few survivors, with more coming forward after the media took an interest. When I suggested questioning Ryan about his knowledge of other clergy, Troy was sceptical. Still, I thought it was worth a try. Troy told me of some police issues he encountered during his investigation of Ryan. I would later tell an Inquiry that Troy said, '... beware of the Catholic Mafia'. I had never heard the phrase before. I took him to mean some police may place loyalty to the Church above their duty. Troy would go on to vehemently deny he ever used the phrase to me.

Travelling to Junee Correctional Centre in the Riverina, I was led to a cramped interview room. No longer wearing his collar and black robes, Vince Ryan appeared diminutive in prison greens. Sporting two black eyes, he was a beaten man in more ways than one.

'Looks like you walked into a door?'

'Happens all the time. I've got used to it.'

I knew the evil this man had done, but still, I couldn't help feeling a little sorry. Whatever punishments he received in gaol, Ryan felt he deserved it, a kind of penance. He was one of the few who didn't fight his initial charges. Pleading guilty saved his victims the ordeal of giving evidence. A small mercy. We spoke amicably for over an hour, during which time I gained a lot of insight. He had been destined for great things, he told me, until he had 'strayed'.

Again, that soft language. Ryan told me he first became aware of his sexual interest in children when he became a priest. Walking through schools, children aroused him. That's how it started. He knew what he was doing was wrong, but couldn't stop.

As I raised Fletcher and other clergy, Ryan clammed up. Loyalty to his Church was clearly paramount. Ryan shared his presbytery in Cessnock with Father David O'Hearn, who was also later convicted of sexually abusing boys in the coalfields. In 2017, a survivor told me he was sexually abused in the Cessnock Catholic Church presbytery in the presence of more than one priest. Daniel's suspicions of a network were probably right.

John Feenan's statement was the last I took before Fletcher's arrest. The whispers at work and daily interaction with clergy made John feel uncomfortable within the Diocese offices. At work, a priest colleague of Fletcher's told John that Fletcher claimed Daniel never stayed at his presbytery. It was a highly inappropriate comment to a witness in the middle of a criminal investigation. John knew Fletcher's denial was a lie because he dropped Daniel off and picked him up the next morning. John also shared his concerns with me about the fact Bishop Malone had said, 'The matter has to go to the DPP yet, and they may decide not to proceed with this case.'

Malone may have just been explaining a legal process. Still, after the DPP declined to prosecute Monsignor Cotter, John was nervous.

As promised, I notified the Church before Fletcher presented himself at Maitland Police Station on Wednesday, 14 May 2003. Arrest by appointment. Like Pell accompanying Ridsdale to court, Monsignor Jim Saunders now supported Fletcher. A lawyer accompanied them, fully briefed, thanks to Malone's tip-off. There was no clerical collar as Fletcher arrived in a parka and business shirt. With Saunders also appearing in civilian attire, it seemed to me that they didn't want to draw anyone's attention to that day's events. Fletcher studied the detective before him. Yes, we had seen each other before.

Fletcher denied the allegations. That was predictable. He also minimised intimacy with the Feenans. This didn't overtly affect the case; there was plenty of evidence to the contrary. The fact that Fletcher confirmed that Daniel had spent a night at his Branxton presbytery left me wondering if someone had pointed out to him that John was a witness. Fletcher also stated he had no idea who called him the night of the *60 Minutes* story – that is, until Bishop Malone warned him of my investigation. Fletcher didn't appear upset and answered my questions in a matter-of-fact manner. With a lawyer and senior churchman beside him, and knowing he had the support of parishioners and his Church, he appeared confident. There was no sign of anger or distress as Fletcher denied all the allegations of his criminal acts. Beyond that, his interview was benign.

Fletcher's arrest and police charging was pretty much routine. I took him to the Maitland Court House to be formally charged. Fletcher had already been stood down, but I wanted bail conditions to keep him away from children, which were granted.

Although events at the station were routine, what happened at court was another matter. After finalising Fletcher's charges at the police station I now needed to put him before the magistrate at Maitland Court House for a bail determination. Briefing the police prosecutor, he told me he grew up in one of Fletcher's parishes. In the Hunter everyone seems to know everyone.

'Is that an issue?' I asked him.

He assured me it wasn't. I instructed the prosecutor that I wasn't opposing bail, but I insisted on conditions to keep Fletcher away from children. It was straightforward stuff.

Late in the day the court was almost empty. I sat in the back on one of those hard timber benches. It didn't matter, this wouldn't take long.

The charge sheets were handed up without being read aloud. A departure from the norm, but not unusual considering their nature. The prosecutor declared knowing Fletcher. He had been an altar boy in one of the priest's parishes. I had no issue with that being placed on the record. It was only right to let the court know, however the prosecutor now embarked on something altogether different. Fletcher was a good man, he told the court. He had cared for parishioners and did wonderful community work. I had been in court enough to realise this wasn't usual. Fletcher had his own solicitor to provide evidence of good character. If not for protocols, I would have stood up and objected. Remaining in my seat I determined to have a word with the prosecutor when this ended.

The prosecutor then deviated further, requesting a total suppression order to prevent media from reporting Fletcher's name and his being a Catholic priest. I was gobsmacked. On my feet before I knew it, I almost ran. I wasn't going to allow the hearing to be hijacked. I had given no instruction for a suppression order; it would be counter-productive – I knew publicity would encourage others to come forward, as it eventually did.

I stormed to the bar table, but the prosecutor steadfastly did not look at me. I moved closer. 'What the hell do you think you're doing?' I said. 'I don't want a suppression order.'

He ignored me. Noticing the commotion, the Magistrate cut him short, rejecting his requested suppression order. Incensed, I waited for court to finish. I would now have more than just a word. I fumed when the court adjourned and the prosecutor joined senior clergy and Fletcher's solicitor.

At the police station I made a formal complaint to the Crime Manager, who explained the prosecutor didn't fall under his authority. I had to submit a report.

'No problem.' I told him.

I wasn't the only one outraged. No sooner did I start typing than the phone rang. A journalist also wanted to complain.

'Stand in line,' I told her.

It turned out the journalist was denied information on the nature of Fletcher's charges. There was no suppression order, so the press had a right to know. I offered to read the charges over the phone, but there was more. When the journalist phoned the Maitland–Newcastle Diocese they were told a comment would not be forthcoming. A spokesperson said they expected Fletcher's name and the fact he was a priest to be supressed.

I added the journalist's name and information to my complaint and submitted my report. I also wrote up what occurred in my duty book. Around this time I made another phone call to Troy Grant at Dubbo, telling him the result of my interview with Vince Ryan in Junee Gaol and what happened at court with Fletcher.

With Fletcher's arrest complete, I started gathering statements about the night Daniel threw bottles at the presbytery. In a phone call, Father Robert Searle told me: 'He [Daniel] seemed to be angry with the world that night, and in light of what has now come out, that may be understandable.'

Searle was more than willing to discuss Daniel yelling about priests doing, 'filthy things to little boys'.

This accorded with Pat's recollection of Searle's phone call to her. I noted everything Searle said in that phone call but three days later, what was provided in an official statement was different. Daniel's remark about priests and little boys was recorded as, 'Nobody loves me.'

My dealings with Church officials didn't improve when Father Des Harrigan refused to include specific events in his statement, such as what Fletcher told him about the abusive telephone call the morning after it occurred. Father Burston couldn't recall any discussion with John Feenan in which Fletcher was alleged to have said Daniel never stayed overnight at the Branxton presbytery. Monsignor Saunders couldn't remember if he told Bishop Malone of Daniel's phone call to Fletcher. All were symptomatic of what I would see as systemic clergy failures of memory before the Child Abuse Royal Commission.

I had taken note of police lessons of the past regarding the value of media exposure in these cases, and as such I argued with the prosecutor against a suppression order. Subsequently, media coverage resulted in more of Fletcher's victims coming forward.

One witness remembered Bishop Malone asking why a teacher had warned 'not to leave boys alone with Fletcher'.

That teacher was Patrick Roohan, who had also warned the Diocese about Fletcher's behaviour around young boys.

These two statements conflicted with Malone telling me he had no concerns about Fletcher 'before John Feenan approached me'. In fairness to Malone, after Fletcher's arrest he did volunteer Roohan's concerns, although didn't explain why he and Saunders couldn't recall it earlier.

I passed all this information on to the Ombudsman's investigative team in Sydney who asked for more documents, copies of statements, and Fletcher's interview.

Although anxious about the upcoming trial, Daniel's health improved. Despite peripheral evidence, the trial would still boil down to Daniel's word against Fletcher's. That's when Pat Feenan started receiving menacing late-night phone calls.

Reading about the charges, a parishioner who had helped Fletcher pack up his belongings before leaving the Lochinvar presbytery, contacted me. He had found homosexual pornographic material among Fletcher's other belongings at the presbytery. Were the young men in the images underage? He couldn't say. Fletcher snatched them off him, saying they belonged to the priest who resided there before him.

Father Des Harrigan was the Lochinvar priest before Fletcher. Phoning ahead, I arrived at his Raymond Terrace presbytery the next morning. He didn't move from his lounge chair, merely looking through the screen door to beckon me inside. No effort was made to conceal the alcohol on his breath or the bottle beside him. I knew he and Fletcher continued to have a close relationship.

'I have been told that after you left Lochinvar Presbytery and Jim Fletcher moved in, a number of homosexual pornographic magazines and videos were found in that presbytery,' I said. 'I need to know if those items belonged to you or Father Fletcher.'

Without batting an eyelid Harrigan said, 'They were mine.'

'Are you sure?'

Becoming upset, his voice quivered as he shed tears, 'Yes.'

'Do you have them? Did Jim Fletcher hand them back to you?'

'Yes, he did, and I have destroyed them.'

My questions continued, with Harrigan crying further as he conceded Fletcher probably owned similar material. When he composed himself I asked why he destroyed the material. He said he didn't know. I was aware possession of adult pornography wasn't illegal, but still, the Church might not have been impressed about their clergy sharing such material. Harrigan's memory then failed. He said he couldn't remember if he left his pornography at Lochinvar by mistake or loaned it to Fletcher.

When he asked when all this was going to end, I said, 'I suppose when allegations stop of clergy sexually abusing children.'

I let myself out.

CHAPTER 12

THE GOOD PRIEST

I have no idea if it was standard practice, but when I learned the Ombudsman had provided the Catholic Church with its investigation report into the Church's own failings, I too requested a copy. Having instigated their investigation and provided reams of documents to them, I thought the report might have been able to assist with Fletcher's upcoming trial. The Ombudsman refused to provide me with a copy, telling me I wasn't the complainant. Well, if I wasn't the complainant, who was?

I reasoned that Pat Feenan, being the mother of Daniel, a minor at the time of the offences, and the person who had phoned St Brigid's School at Branxton to discover Fletcher was still visiting and tutoring children, had to be that person. To our dismay, Pat too was refused a copy. So, the offending institution was entitled to the report, but not those who complained? To this day, I don't know if the report could have assisted or not. It made no sense. In 2012, Pat Feenan's book publisher was contacted by the Ombudsman anxious to know if Pat had said anything in her book about the Ombudsman's refusal to provide us with their report.

•

As Fletcher's 2004 trial date neared, another priest asked to see me. Following my previous dealings with clergy, I was now more wary. I needn't have been. I came to refer to this man as *the good priest*. Glen Walsh had only become a priest eight years earlier after a career in teaching. We liked each other from the start. Over the years Glen and I would share our thoughts on clergy abuse and its concealment as we took one another into confidence.

I was taken aback when Glen disclosed he knew of a second victim of Fletcher. This survivor had spoken to his family as an indirect consequence of the media reporting on Fletcher's charges and Fletcher approaching the survivor's sister for a court reference. Glen would later give evidence that the Diocese told him, 'Don't do anything about it.'

Judge Elliot would later equate this as Glen being told to 'bury it'.

Malone urged Glen to bring the survivor to him and in the interim provide him with the Towards Healing helpline number. There was no mention of police. Without telling Malone, Glen approached me.

With Fletcher's trial only weeks away, this second survivor's evidence would prove crucial, but Glen didn't have permission to provide his name. Whoever this survivor was, I needed to speak to him, and soon. Glen promised to do what he could. I could have demanded Glen provide the survivor's details there and then. Legally he was obliged. In the time we had spoken, I was confident Glen would do his best.

My trust wasn't misplaced. Glen soon put me in contact with the survivor, whom I will call Adam (not his real name). Unsure what he wanted to do, Adam at least agreed to talk.

That's when the Church learned what Glen had done. From this point, Glen was effectively cut off from his Church. He didn't use the word *ostracised*, but others did. It wasn't long before this good priest was forced to leave the Diocese.

•

When Adam and I first met, his disclosure was still raw. He hadn't told his family everything and was unsure if he would. His sister, whom I will call Holly, and his mother had entertained suspicions. Adam and Holly will continue to feature later in this story. When Fletcher had requested a character reference from Holly for his upcoming trial, Adam protested, insisting his sister not do so. As Adam opened up to his mother about what Fletcher had done, Father Glen Walsh unexpectedly walked in.

Adam was prepared to talk with me, but that was all. As I had done with Daniel, I put everything on the table. I went through the options and possible outcomes. I didn't push, leaving all the decisions to Adam.

Adam eventually agreed to tell me his story and provide a statement, but was adamant he didn't want to pursue his own charges. The similarity of Adam's abuse to Daniel's was remarkable. Adam was a few years older than Daniel and neither knew each other, negating any suggestion of collusion.

I now had a dilemma. I had never pushed an abuse survivor to do anything against their will. It was Adam's decision not to pursue criminal charges. I could have charged Fletcher with the crimes against Adam and issued Adam with a subpoena to give evidence, but ethically and professionally I would never do that. Although disappointed, I respected his decision. It meant the jury in Fletcher's trial would never get to know about

Fletcher sexually abusing Adam. It would still come down to Daniel's word against Fletcher's. That's how the law works.

I knew of a relatively untested area of the law, called *Tendency and Coincidence* or *Evidence of Similar Acts*. It involved convincing a judge to allow comparable evidence at another's trial. This is a rather simplified explanation without getting bogged down in legal technicalities. The reality was more complicated.

I explained all this to Adam as best I could, then gave him time to think it over. Days later Adam agreed to help, on one condition: he and his family remain anonymous. Convincing the DPP about the merit of Adam's evidence, it was agreed to defer Fletcher's trial. It wasn't an easy decision, because Daniel and his family were already anxious. I couldn't say too much, other than another victim of Fletcher had come forward and his evidence might assist Daniel. Daniel wasn't surprised to learn there were other survivors of Fletcher's abuse. He took the news more calmly than I expected. Pat, John and his brothers were of course saddened to learn another boy had been abused, but pleased knowing that if Adam's evidence was allowed, Daniel's allegations stood a better chance of convincing a jury. If I told Daniel's family too much, I explained, it might jeopardise Adam's evidence and raise suggestions of collusion. They just had to trust me.

There was no template for the evidence I proposed putting together. I spent hours phoning lawyers and consulting law books, legislation and case law online. My submission took weeks to finalise, drawing parallels between Daniel's and Adam's evidence: grooming methods and family relationships, nature of the offences, words and phrases used by Fletcher, smutty jokes and crime locations. Both had been altar boys of a similar age when the abuse occurred. Fletcher had shown

Adam pornographic material, not dissimilar to those he had shown Pat and John Feenan. I put together everything I could think of, but it would still come down to a judge's discretion.

As I obtained statements from Adam's family, I saw that their likeness to the Feenans was uncanny. There was also the unexpected. Adam's father said Fletcher disclosed going to see Vince Ryan after the latter's arrest. Parking in a side street, Fletcher decided not to go in. There were too many people. 'I didn't want to be recognised.'

Holly and her mother also told me that Archbishop Philip Wilson had told them that Fletcher's arrest had shocked him. After being told about Adam being abused, Wilson inquired what Adam intended to do. Wilson remembered Holly and Adam hanging around the Maitland Bishop's residence as kids when Wilson had resided there with Fletcher.

Cast out of the Maitland–Newcastle Diocese, Father Glen Walsh went to see Cardinal George Pell about returning to a teaching position in Sydney. Glen never told me everything about the meeting, but I know he was later given a teaching position. Arriving at Sydney's St Mary Cathedral for the meeting, Glen told me he was walking down a corridor when Philip Wilson happened to bump into him. Years later I would learn of other contact between Glen and Wilson involving Fletcher.

After Adam, a third survivor came forward. Peter Gogarty was a lot older, his allegations from more than a decade before Daniel's abuse. Peter believed that Fletcher had also abused others and insisted on giving a statement to assist in Fletcher's trial.

I spoke to other possible survivors. One broke into tears intimating Fletcher had done something, but didn't want to discuss it. He knew of the Feenans' ostracism, explaining he didn't want to expose his family to similar treatment. Talking to potential witnesses, I learned this possible survivor's parents had a falling out with Fletcher just before the Diocese moved Fletcher to Gateshead in 1983.

It wasn't long before Adam's family experienced similar ostracism to the Feenans. Old friends turned their backs while priests snubbed them at church.

Meanwhile, the Diocese extended a loan for Fletcher's legal defence, and parishioners made donations. Pat learned that one priest in the Diocese donated his parish Christmas collection to Fletcher's legal defence fund. A Vincentian, the priest had been a teacher at St Stanislaus' College in Bathurst before moving to the Maitland–Newcastle Diocese. I knew St Stanislaus had a horrendous record of child sexual abuse, with more than 160 boys falling victim at the school since the 1970s, so I did some digging. In response to an initial child sexual abuse allegation a second boy came forward. The Vincentians acted quickly, apologising for 'any harm experienced by you while you were in our care'.

The boy was paid compensation on signing a deed of release. Like Joan Isaacs, the girl sexually abused by Father Derriman in Brisbane and who later had to fight the Church's Towards Healing system in court, it meant he couldn't discuss his abuse with anyone. If this survivor breached the deed, he had to repay his compensation at ten percent interest per annum. Hush money. A detective recorded his frustration on the police COPS system when the complaint was withdrawn.

The priest, however, was accepted into the Maitland–Newcastle Diocese and placed in the same parish where Fletcher abused Daniel. Parishioners weren't told of his background. When Pat and I complained about the donation to Fletcher's legal defence, and the priest's questionable history, Malone took action and the priest was immediately stood down.

•

Daniel and Adam, and their families, were kept apart to prevent evidence being contaminated. They knew of each other's existence, but that was all.

Queen's Counsels never come cheap. Fletcher, supported by Church finance, employed Ian Barker QC, the lawyer said to have convicted Lindy Chamberlain by exonerating the dingo. The trial started on 23 November 2004.

Referred to as a trial within a trial, a *voir dire* was conducted to decide if the evidence of Peter Gogarty and Adam would be allowed. Judge Armitage ruled that Peter's allegations, of ephemeral touching outside his clothing, was too dissimilar to the abuse of Daniel and Adam, so disallowed it. Peter was disappointed, but he had tried.

Barker used every legal argument he could muster to exclude Adam's tendency and coincidence evidence, but all our hard work paid off when Judge Armitage allowed it. It was a landmark decision.

I didn't see Daniel give evidence. I couldn't go in until after I had given mine. Pat, John, Daniel's brothers and extended family were all in the same position. There were best wishes, hugs and tears as Daniel walked into court. When the door closed, Pat and John were comforted by family and friends.

Although I couldn't be inside, I knew Daniel would do well. Ian Barker wouldn't go easy, but I was confident Daniel was up to it.

Time passed slowly outside. I spent most of it reassuring and instructing other witnesses not to discuss evidence with Daniel until their own evidence was complete. With the lunch adjournment, the door swung open. A sea of faces exited, with many in tears. Then came Daniel. We couldn't talk, but

I was told he was doing well. I had sat though evidence like Daniel's. It's never easy. Everyone is uncomfortable listening to what happened, but none more so than the person in the witness box.

Fletcher's entourage followed him back and forth. I saw many venomous looks the survivors and their families had to endure.

At long last Daniel's evidence ended, to be followed by family and other witnesses later in the week. On the afternoon Pat gave evidence, she walked back into the witness room shaken.

'Are you all right?'

She wasn't. In the bathroom one of Fletcher's supporters had spun around, knocking Pat sideways with her head striking the wall. Ropable, I wanted her to pursue charges. Pat declined, saying she couldn't rule out it being an accident.

'Did she stop and apologise?'

'Well, no.'

Pat insisted she wanted nothing done.

I notified court staff and Fletcher's legal team. They wouldn't have condoned what happened, but they could ensure there was no repeat.

Priests and Church officials walked past our rooms to join Fletcher's entourage, where I heard those in the room saying prayers for Father Jim. Rooms those priests walked past were full of the survivors' families, all good Catholics and regular churchgoers. Not one of these men of God stopped to offer them their support, let alone a prayer.

My turn in the witness box didn't come until the second week. Fletcher's legal team decided their client would not give evidence, so his recorded interview with me would be the only opportunity for the jury to hear him.

It was now Adam's turn in the witness box. Like Daniel, he was surrounded by family and love.

Adam's evidence contained so many similarities to Daniel's, it had to have an impact. That's why Barker fought so hard to exclude it. Adam and Daniel had never met, yet their descriptions of what Fletcher did to them were almost identical.

When Adam picked up the bible to be sworn in, I knew what was coming. I didn't just see the reaction, I heard it too. It was a similarity I didn't need to spell out. The jury gasped as they shuffled in their seats, as did the gallery. Adam could have been mistaken for Daniel's brother. Jurors glanced at Daniel in the back of the court to make sure they weren't seeing things. The same height, physique and boyish good looks. And those eyes, oh those eyes. Nothing further needed to be said.

Fletcher targeted specific boys with specific looks. Unlike Vince Ryan and Gerald Ridsdale who targeted as many boys as they could, Fletcher was selective.

Adam was no fool, his intellect on a par with Daniel's. As the prosecutor led his evidence, Adam told the court he had also been an altar boy when Fletcher began sexually abusing him from the age of thirteen. Like Daniel, Adam was also sexually abused in a church presbytery.

Fletcher listened, but he never lifted his head during Adam's evidence.

Of course, Barker suggested Adam was making it all up. That was Barker's job. To discredit the witness he had to find a motive. Adam knew what to expect. When Barker asked Adam if he had made a claim for compensation, Adam replied, 'No.'

When asked if he intended to make a claim, Adam's answer was another emphatic, 'No.'

The reason he was giving evidence, Adam explained, was because it was the truth. Barker had nowhere to go. He had committed the lawyer's ultimate sin by asking a question to which he didn't already know the answer.

Both legal teams summed up before the judge instructed the jury. All we could do now was wait.

The Feenans were now permitted to speak with the other family, sharing their grief and support. The embrace shared by Daniel and Adam bought many to tears. Even I choked a little. Adam's evidence was selfless. I have no idea what he and Daniel discussed as they walked about the lawns. Only they knew what the other had been through.

There was nothing I could now do but walk under the jacaranda trees' last flush of purple or sit on the witness room floor playing cards with Daniel's brothers.

When the jury retired, more media arrived. There was a wave of excitement when someone said the jury was returning. It turned out the four women and eight men only had a question. 'Is it unusual for a Catholic priest to serve in so many parishes?'

It was a great question, with the judge telling jurors to make of it whatever they thought. I believe the question showed a growing awareness of what was happening. The jury left and I went back to pacing corridors.

The trial entered its third week, but still no verdict. The jury didn't rush, giving everything full consideration. Seventeen hours into their deliberations word arrived. The jury had reached a verdict.

Donna sat beside Daniel. Luke Feenan was on his other side with an arm around his brother. Pat too was surrounded by family. She looked at Daniel with a mother's reassurance. Whatever the verdict, she believed him. I had my hand on Pat's shoulder with her hand on mine. Words were superfluous.

The East Maitland Court House filled to overflowing. We stood for the judge and watched the jury file in. No matter how often I had been there, this part was never easy. My stomach tightened as my heart thumped harder. The foreperson stood as she was asked if the jury had reached their decision.

'We have, Your Honour.'

Fletcher stood with his head bowed. I had no sympathy. He had made Daniel and Adam go through this ordeal of reliving their pain. Some jurors looked towards the survivors and their families. Few, if any, looked at the priest. I hoped it was a good sign. The advocate read the charges, one at a time.

'How do you find the accused, guilty or not guilty?'

'Guilty.'

A collective sigh. Pat broke into tears as she looked at her son. Daniel sat upright, attentive, his facial expression unmoved. As the guilty verdicts accumulated, Pat raised a finger for each. Tears flowed freely down her face. A third guilty, followed by a fourth. Someone pointed out that the foreperson wasn't holding any notes, so only needed to remember one word. A fifth guilty followed until Pat held nine fingers upright. Guilty on all counts. There were muffled cries and supressed clapping as Fletcher was led away.

Hugging Daniel, Pat pointed out that Luke was the more emotional. Matter-of-factly Daniel replied, 'But Mum, I knew he was guilty.'

Outside, there were tears, handshakes and hugs. As the outpouring of emotion continued, the media respectfully stepped back. When Daniel's youngest brother, Bernard, embraced me, Pat cried some more and joined us. Luke wrapped his arms around Daniel like he would never let go. Daniel and Adam had shown enormous courage and dignity, and I told them no less. Pat and John embraced one another as I walked over to Adam's family, where the hugs continued.

That night, Pat's and Holly's houses were both egged, and the paintwork on the car belonging to another of Adam's sisters was scratched. It seemed not everyone was happy with the verdict.

Fletcher's conviction was the lead story on television and radio throughout the Hunter. The following morning it was splashed across newspapers. Bishop Malone faced difficult questions as to why he hadn't removed Fletcher earlier.

Emboldened by Daniel's and Adam's courage, more of the Hunter's survivors came forward, resulting in further clergy coming under investigation. As the outrage grew, Malone responded by announcing a Diocesan Child Protection Unit. The government and police hierarchy applauded the Church as those authorities deferred to the Church and stepped back from any further response.

In April 2005, Judge Armitage sentenced Fletcher to a minimum seven and a half years' gaol. Ian Barker appealed, arguing the judge shouldn't have permitted the tendency and coincidence evidence.

The NSW Court of Criminal Appeal sits over the District and Supreme Courts. Fletcher's appeal was heard before three judges, one of whom was Justice Peter McClellan, who a decade later would become chair of the Child Abuse Royal Commission. Members of Daniel's and Adam's families travelled to Sydney for the hearing. Their Honours determined the trial judge's decision to allow the tendency and coincidence evidence was correct. Fletcher's appeal was dismissed.

Money was no object as Fletcher next appealed to the High Court of Australia, however on 6 January 2006, Fletcher died in gaol from natural causes.

Fletcher's funeral, across the road from the scene of one of his crimes in Branxton, was attended by more than thirty priests.

His headstone at Sandgate Cemetery read like an honour board, omitting any mention of his crimes or convictions.

With Fletcher's death one might have expected an end to the appeals. Extraordinarily, the executor of Fletcher's estate, a fellow priest, pushed ahead with the High Court appeal. In March 2006, Ian Barker again argued to have the tendency and coincidence evidence rejected. Chief Justice Murray Gleeson and Justice Kenneth Hayne disagreed with Barker: 'We are not persuaded there has been any miscarriage of justice'.

Survivors and their families were elated. All our hard work in formulating the tendency and coincidence evidence had paid off. I told a waiting media: 'This decision means that the highest court in the land accepts as correct for the District Court to have allowed evidence from a second altar boy whom Fletcher abused, and that will flow on to all other courts so they too can accept similar tendency evidence.'

Detectives began approaching me, some referred by the DPP and others of their own accord. Thereafter I was happy to assist all with their tendency and coincidence evidence. Fletcher's appeal had backfired; it established a legal precedent to be used in all future similar trials, not just in NSW, but throughout Australia.

•

Bishop Malone hired Helen Keevers to manage his new Child Protection Unit. Helen and I would become friends as she would go on to play a major role in future events, of which you will read more about later. Our first meeting, at Fletcher's sentencing, however, got off to a bumpy start. She being a Church employee, and me tending to be blunt, I told Helen she would have to earn my trust. Helen didn't flinch, declaring she would do just that, and she did. Helen was an atheist with a wealth of experience in the welfare profession. She didn't need to be Christian to have those admirable qualities.

Months later, Helen called to say she had located Denis McAlinden being treated for cancer in Perth. It was no secret that NSW Police wanted to speak with him. It has never been explained to me how he was paid a Church stipend and living in a Catholic care facility, yet before Helen arrived no one notified police.

I organised for a WA police officer to visit. He confirmed McAlinden was dying of cancer and couldn't be extradited. Updating McAlinden's case, I telephoned Annette. It had been six years since she provided Mark Watters with her statement of sexual abuse at the hands of McAlinden. Her husband explained she wasn't well, but appreciated me letting him know. He told me that Bishop Clarke and other clergy knew of his wife's abuse prior to 1995, which was when Wilson dealt with Anthea and Denise, but he was at a loss as to why the Church never passed this information on to police. McAlinden was never defrocked and died a priest two weeks later. Justice being denied was the price his victims paid for the Church avoiding another scandal.

In 2004, with hundreds more allegations of child sexual abuse at Morisset emerging, I submitted my first report through the police chain of command to the Sex Crimes Squad for the Catholic Church to be examined, particularly for the crime of concealing child sexual abuse.

Hearing nothing from my first report, I submitted another. I regret having not kept copies, as you will read, my reports were not able to be found later.

•

Penny and I always cared about children. Penny chaired a community aid panel to rehabilitate kids appearing at court, while I was vice-president of a local youth refuge. So, when Helen Keevers opened Zimmerman House as part of the Diocese's Child Protection Unit, I took up her invitation to visit. Going through the Diocese's archives, Helen told me, not everything sat well with her, although she was keen to say that Bishop Malone had changed since Fletcher's conviction. Maybe so, but the number of survivors coming forward said volumes. We agreed to disagree. Meanwhile, I heard nothing back about my reports from police hierarchy.

CHAPTER 13

THE BROTHERHOOD

At the beginning of this book I mentioned that various factors beyond clergy abuse played a part in my speaking out. To explain those factors, I need to digress. I initially wrote this chapter using real names. To avoid suggestions I have an axe to grind, I have replaced names in this chapter with pseudonyms. My motive is for you, the reader, to understand the police culture and my reasons for going outside the police force to speak about clergy abuse.

Police investigating police remains contentious, causing many to be sceptical. The reality is, police will always draw complaints, some credible and many unfounded. When I first joined the police force, stories abounded of people who made complaints against police being unceremoniously frog-marched out of the inspector's office. Police didn't want to investigate their peers, and fewer still wanted to work in Internal Affairs.

The Police Royal Commission exposed the Office of Professional Responsibility and its Internal Affairs predecessor as incompetent. To help shed that stigma, it was renamed Professional Standards. Promotional opportunities were offered, so police were now keener to transfer to the unit. It looked good on a resume. My experience was that little had changed, with many investigators lacking vigour. With the volume of investigations most complaints continue to be handed back to commands, meaning complaints against police are investigated by colleagues rather than someone independent. Like it or not, police continue to investigate police.

It is primarily the officer conducting an internal investigation who controls its integrity and outcome. Police are trained to conduct internal investigations, but that doesn't guarantee officers won't be inept, lazy or unethical. Most are capable but weighed down by workloads. The good horse always gets flogged. Even when an investigator is conscientious, they are watched by fellow officers. Nothing is said, but you know that quiet discussions are being had. At the end of the day, investigators have to work with those police again. It's the unspoken factor: police still don't like investigating police.

The Brotherhood identified by Justice Wood in his 1990 Royal Commission into the NSW Police Force didn't disappear after he wrote his report; it just went underground for a while.

•

In the late 1990s, I received a call from my superintendent. A civilian police employee alleged she had been indecently assaulted in a police station toilet. I knew the alleged offender, a popular officer with whom I had worked. In fact, we had played rugby together, sharing a few drinks after games. I declared a conflict of interest, believing I should have been disqualified, but Newcastle's assistant commissioner instructed me to continue. Be that as it may, I was resolute to conduct an impartial investigation.

When I criminally charged the officer, many police were unhappy. With no independent witnesses, the case boiled down to the officer's word against that of the complainant. Unable to be proven beyond a reasonable doubt, the officer was acquitted. A civil case, however, succeeded and he was dismissed from the force. My name was mud. I didn't care, I never doubted the complainant. What the superintendent and assistant commissioner didn't tell me at the time was that the accused, when still a serving police officer at the time of the indecent assault allegation, had been under house arrest while he was awaiting trial on allegations he had sexually abused his nieces.

•

It was never my plan to become a commissioned officer. I loved being a detective sergeant too much. In late 2004 I missed out on a senior sergeant promotion in my office. I had been too absorbed with the Fletcher trial and other investigations. Re-evaluating my position I decided to apply for commissioned rank. By 2005 I had obtained an interview for a professional standards inspector's position. I walked out of the interview confident, having nailed every question. I scored well above everyone else, but by 2006 I still hadn't been awarded the position. I started asking questions, but there were no answers. The Region Commander refused to meet with me.

Promotion could mean an increase of tens of thousands of dollars in annual salary and an elevation in power. In the police force, controlling promotion meant controlling power. It was supposed to be governed by semi-independent processes – a 2003 Ministerial Inquiry, the Schuberg Report, introduced-'Integrity in Promotion' – but nepotism still abounded.

Six months after the interviews, the position was withdrawn and given to an officer who hadn't applied for it. I was furious.

Colleagues would say I was like a dog with a bone when it came to investigating. I now poured that energy into finding out what occurred surrounding my failed promotion. The more I dug, the more irregularities I uncovered with senior police ducking and weaving.

Catching a senior public servant off guard, his voice quivered. That's when I first heard the term *secretly disqualified*, as he insisted what occurred had nothing to do with him. Whatever happened was hidden within Professional Standards, the very unit entrusted with ethics and integrity.

When I told the police union I was considering going public with what I had uncovered, I was suddenly invited to a meeting in the commissioner's boardroom.

My superintendent now asked lots of questions. When I said I was bringing a witness to the meeting, he suggested the meeting might be called off.

At 3.55 p.m. on Thursday, 27 July 2006, I walked into the commissioner's boardroom with a union representative. My superintendent, two assistant commissioners and a deputy commissioner were already inside. I won't go into detail about what happened, that's another story, suffice to say most police would be horrified. As I was leaving, an odd thing happened. The assistant commissioner in charge of Professional Standards leaned over and quietly told me he felt positive about my applying for another promotion. Was that a wink and a nod?

I know that what happened to me wasn't an isolated incident. Most police would have no idea what went on to side-step independent appeal processes.

The next interview committee I went before was chaired by the same superintendent from the commissioner's boardroom.

After the interview, I told Penny I didn't stand a chance, I'd blown two questions.

My dad was in a nearby palliative care unit dying from cancer the day of my interview. Waiting for visiting hours to begin, Penny and I sat outside the interview room. When the interview committee packed up and left, it hit me: I was the first and last person to be interviewed. Sure, there could have been other interviews another day, but to convene a committee for just me was unusual.

It was announced I had won the promotion. Impossible. Was this the wink and the nod? I wanted to decline, but Penny reasoned I had fairly won a promotion, maybe not this one, but ...

A conscience can be a difficult thing. Having recorded what happened in the commissioner's boardroom, I documented everything. I knew it might cost me a promotion, but I sent complaints to the Independent Commission against Corruption, the Police Integrity Commission and the Ombudsman. It was pointless complaining to Professional Standards; they were involved. All three agencies declined to investigate. If nothing else, I learned a lot about complaint processes and oversight bodies.

•

By the time I became a detective chief inspector, I had earned a tough reputation for investigating police. Some thought me hard, but I was always fair.

My attitude didn't sit well with everyone, so when handed internal investigations I would caution, 'If you don't want me to go hard, don't give it to me.'

I didn't care what others thought, I wasn't prepared to bend the rules because someone was a cop.

What I want to convey is that past events and experiences shaped my thinking as I tried to push the police force to investigate the concealment of child sexual abuse within the Catholic Church. It also shaped my thoughts about complaining to oversight bodies.

•

Fred's size and behaviour intimidated female colleagues. His sexual harassment was so prevalent, policewomen coined a specific term for it. His previous supervisor had started a file, however, his new detective sergeant took an easier approach.

In 2007, Sue worked a late shift with Fred, despite having asked not to work with him. She wasn't the only one to complain about his harassment, but her supervisors failed to report him.

This night, Fred made comments so degrading I won't repeat them, taking a perverted delight in Sue's discomfort.

Sue left early. Upset, she called her detective sergeant, who told her, 'Let me sort this out. That's what I'm paid to do.'

Drummed into police at training days, promotional exams and so on, is that sexual harassment is mandatorily reportable. You don't have a choice, you must report it. But it was kept in-house. In the boys' club, that's how it was done.

Only months earlier the Ronalds Inquiry, a review into police sexual harassment, found that 'sexual harassers were being protected'.

When Commissioner Ken Moroney declared zero tolerance, the opposition police spokesperson, Mike Gallacher, went on the attack. 'You feel like you're in *Groundhog Day* ... We feel like we've been here before discussing this, where we've had these quite startling revelations of sexual harassment ... We've had promise after promise [that] those days are gone. They don't appear to be gone at all.'

Following the Ronalds Inquiry, police were very aware of what was required. Not only did Sue's superior fail to report Fred, he exposed Sue further on the very next shift, asking, 'You okay to work with him tonight?'

Sue reluctantly agreed, provided she could work out of another station. She would only pair up with Fred if necessary. A female colleague told her, 'That is not good enough ... It is unacceptable. If you go back to work and place yourself in that position tonight you are mad. If I was your supervisor, I would be doing a lot more than just speaking to him over this. It needs to be taken further, otherwise this can happen to someone else.'

Still upset by events from the previous evening, Sue again left work early. Her private car was parked at the station where Fred was based but Fred was still on duty there and she was too frightened to collect it. Instead she asked an inspector for a police car to take home. Noticing her distress, the inspector asked what was going on. Sue explained that Martin was taking care of it.

The deeper I dug, the more I found. Fred's behaviour went back years to his previous command. After that, a number of policewomen requested not to be rostered with Fred, yet not one supervisor notified management. Everything was kept within the office.

Fred's behaviour went well beyond sexually harassing colleagues. Police wives and girlfriends were also fair game. A number provided me with statements. Not everyone appreciated the vigour of my investigation, with some police officers telling their wives not to sign their statements.

With the volume of evidence I obtained, Fred had nowhere to go. He hung his head and admitted everything. Sue's superior tried telling me he didn't know he had to report Fred. When I determined he was guilty of failing to act, Sue wasn't happy. Such was the culture. Tackling sexual harassers and those protecting them brought little thanks.

I warned Fred would continue to pose a significant risk. Despite this, Fred was moved to another command and remained a detective. The commissioner's zero tolerance really did sound like *Groundhog Day*.

●

Rob wasn't a bad cop, but he ended up in trouble when it was alleged he assaulted a juvenile. Two detectives determined Rob had done nothing wrong. The Ombudsman didn't see it that way, though, returning their brief for re-investigation.

I first learned of the case when told to review the detective's second investigation. Everything revolved around an Aboriginal teenager at Lemon Tree Passage. I saw nothing wrong with his arrest. The boy had been drinking and resisted police, so he was frog-marched to a police truck. I'd dealt with difficult juveniles too. But, that's where my acquiescence ended.

Hands cuffed behind his back, the boy was placed into a paddy wagon before the door was slammed shut. There was debate whether the boy was still yelling. Rob returned and asked two policewomen I will call Carol and Jan, to open the cage door.

Carol was Rob's friend and had been a police officer for some time. Jan had less service, but was competent.

When the cage door opened, Rob pulled out his pepper spray. Leaning inside, he sprayed the boy's face before slamming the door shut. Hands still cuffed behind his back, the boy was helpless. He couldn't wipe his face to lessen the stinging, and the vapour's effect was magnified in the confined space.

I've been hit with pepper spray myself, and I can tell you, it's not fun.

In disbelief, the policewomen drove to a service station and applied water to lessen the boy's discomfort. An inspector was called and a complaint was lodged with Rob directed not to speak to the witnesses.

The policewomen considered what Rob did wrong, but both were uneasy. Rob ignored the inspector's direction in attempting to speak with Carol on no fewer than three occasions. That's when ranks closed and both women felt the displeasure of colleagues.

Despite the Ombudsman's concerns, the detectives returned their re-investigation findings unaltered.

When the file came back, I was told to take over the initial alleged assault investigation and also to investigate the role of the two detectives.

Carol and Jan were upset. They had no faith in the detectives or the investigation they conducted. Carol used the term 'boys' club' to describe their investigation. Jan was just as distressed and felt the station had turned against her.

I sent the brief to the DPP resulting in Rob being criminally charged.

A number of police sat in court supporting Rob, at the same time intimidating Carol and Jan. Both policewomen gave evidence. They saw no reason for Rob's action. Rob was convicted, but his conviction was overturned on appeal.

The commissioner of police was privy to information the appeal court did not have. Based on this, Rob was dismissed from the police force.

Carol and Jan paid a heavy price. I too felt some ostracism, but my rank afforded me some protection. Carol suffered terribly and was eventually discharged as medically unfit. A good officer lost.

Jan's treatment was just as spiteful. I had no hesitation helping her transfer out of the area. We lost contact, but I hope she's doing well.

•

After Carol and Jan's treatment, it was my turn. In 2008, four years after Fletcher's conviction and two years before I started re-examining the McAlinden and Fletcher cover-ups, the new Region Commander transferred me from Maitland to Newcastle where I was berated for my conduct of the pepper-spraying investigation. Apparently my holding police accountable for assaulting a teenage boy wasn't appreciated.

I was also to receive a Region Commander's warning notice. A fairly serious black mark in my file. But for what?

I was never told what I had done wrong, nor given an opportunity to respond.

I hadn't been a detective for thirty years without acquiring some knowledge of the law. I was entitled to procedural fairness. My report to the Ombudsman threw a spanner in what I believe was supposed to be a quick execution.

The superintendent who was assigned to interview me just kept saying this was my chance to respond. Respond to what? I shook my head asking how I could respond if

I wasn't going to be told what I'd done wrong. This bizarre exercise just kept going in circles until he eventually ended the interview.

A review within the Region Office determined I had done wrong, but didn't spell out any specifics. To me, this seemed just as farcical as the interview conducted by the superintendent.

The Region Commander now declared procedural fairness had been met and I was transferred to Raymond Terrace.

In my complaint I described the content of the Region Commander's warning notice as *gobbledygook*. I was berated, transferred and disciplined merely for holding a police officer to account for what I considered an unlawful assault of a defenceless Aboriginal boy.

I suffered ridicule and embarrassment for years, until my objections landed on the desk of Deputy Commissioner Nick Kaldas. I had never met Nick Kaldas, but his reputation for fairness and integrity preceded him. He was sufficiently alarmed to send for the entire dossier on me being disciplined.

Important documents had gone missing, or never existed. Police lawyers assigned to review the file agreed no real examination of my investigation was ever conducted. An officer, who left the police force prior to the investigation, was cited as the complainant. I now learned for the first time that before the new Region Commander took over, I was to be commended for my investigation. That recommendation had been supressed as I somehow went from hero to villain.

Nick Kaldas determined no evidence existed for any adverse finding against me. Put simply, I'd done nothing wrong; in fact, my investigation was commendable. Police lawyers determined I was never afforded procedural fairness, with senior officers found in need of training. I'm not sure a lack of training was the real issue.

The warning notice was revoked and I received a written apology.

In 2012 Penny and I attended Newcastle Police Station where Mr Kaldas personally apologised for the wrongs I had suffered. Unfortunately my transfer and the ridicule I had endured couldn't be undone.

•

Not all of my internal investigations attracted negative repercussions, and I don't want to give the impression everything was sinister. There's always an internal struggle between those trying to do the right thing, and ... well ... those on the other side. Politicians know police scandals aren't good for public confidence. *Operation Retz,* examining police failure to act against prominent paedophiles, was one example of the public being protected from the truth. In police circles I heard it referred to as the Chamber of Dark Secrets. Even Nick Kaldas couldn't fight those forces when he tried to expose illegal police buggings, ultimately resigning.

The point is, by 2012 I had little faith in complaint systems. The higher I rose, the more I saw. It all influenced how I responded to the clergy child abuse scandal and what I believed was police failure to investigate the concealment of those crimes.

CHAPTER 14

THE BRUSH-OFF

The number of Catholic priests, brothers and lay teachers appearing before Hunter courts continued to grow. Father Peter Brock OAM, was an accomplished musician and prominent Hunter priest. When charged with the sexual abuse of nine-year-old twin boys, Brock was stood down. At the same time, Father John Denham faced a further 134 offences relating to thirty-nine boys at St Pius X High School. A number of Denham's former students had died through suicide or drug overdose. In sentencing Denham, Judge Helen Smyth alluded to the cover-up when she said, 'The ability of the offender to continue offending for so long ... calls into question the role of his supervisors.'

Despite the judge's observations being reported in the media, there was still no response from senior police in respect to the cover-up and protection of paedophile priests in the Hunter. If more was to happen, it would fall to the media.

A journalist at the *Newcastle Herald*, Joanne McCarthy, said it was a profession she stumbled into. The eldest in a large Catholic family, Joanne was outspoken. Writing and talking to survivors, she couldn't help but be affected. As her stories became increasingly passionate, her editor, Chad Watson, conceded it was, 'a significant shift away from traditional, objective journalism'.

Some said that after more than 350 articles, Joanne was obsessed. She wasn't fazed; if obsession was what it took to address the problem, she was happy to wear the badge. With cases in the Hunter continuing to grow, Joanne realised not enough was being done.

I'm told I first met Joanne at James Fletcher's trial in 2004, but she was lost to my memory in a sea of media. We spoke four years later, in 2008, when she rang about Father David O'Hearn. I knew nothing about him, so the call was brief. Joanne would later say I gave her the brush-off, which was probably right. Minutes later, I fielded an angry phone call from a fellow officer. He was one of those fast-talking, assertive individuals who spoke over the top of others.

He accused me of tipping off Joanne about his office investigating O'Hearn. His presumption was wrong. Had he checked, he would have discovered the Maitland–Newcastle Diocese released a statement the previous day saying O'Hearn was under investigation and had been stood down. That's why Joanne was ringing around. It was that simple. The officer jumping to the wrong conclusion would later have an adverse impact on other events surrounding the Church concealment investigation.

•

By 2010 I'd had a couple of years to settle into Raymond Terrace.

In April 2010, Shaun McLeod attended Raymond Terrace to charge David O'Hearn with a string of further offences against boys at Muswellbrook, Maitland and Windale. The survivors didn't know one another, but all had similar stories.

In 2009, Father David O'Hearn had been charged with the 1990 sexual assault of a boy in Cessnock, a time when O'Hearn was residing with Father Vince Ryan.

In little more than a decade O'Hearn was moved to no fewer than nine parishes, a similar pattern to that which concerned the jury in the trial of James Fletcher. In 2004, the Maitland–Newcastle Diocese investigated O'Hearn instead of passing the investigation on to police. It found claims against him unsustained.

Charges relating to another three abuse survivors were laid against O'Hearn in July 2009. More would follow. Parishioners condemned the survivors and praised their priest.

In August 2009 the Newcastle Herald reported that a fundraiser for O'Hearn had raised $18,000 by auctioning items such as framed football jerseys donated by his supporters.

I had worked with Shaun McLeod at Cessnock. He was a good investigator and a character to boot. His antics and humour was good for morale. A colleague gave Shaun, a Buddhist, a small Buddha statue for his desk. He already had a ceremonial cloth on his wall before pulling out his prayer beads. I said nothing. The next morning, the scent of burning incense wafted through the office. I turned to Shaun, *'I can live with the statue, the cloth and the prayer beads, but Shaun, I am drawing a line at incense and turning this office into a bloody Buddhist temple.'*

Shaun and the others broke into laughter. He had provoked the response they'd sought. Funny bastard.

I was pleased to see Shaun. Based at Charlestown, he was now part of Strike Force Georgiana, which had been investigating clergy child sexual abuse. Shaun was dismayed at the pressure to close Strike Force Georgiana down. He independently determined there was large-scale cover-up of child sexual abuse in the Maitland–Newcastle Diocese. Anyone looking at the bigger picture had to come to the same conclusion.

Shaun explained to me that Edmund Gleeson House in Maitland had accommodated a seminary where Fletcher and O'Hearn trained. Father Francis Donovan, an instructor at the seminary, had sexually abused girls from the adjoining school. Father Peter Quirk had sexually abused boys in Maitland when Fletcher, O'Hearn and Ryan were doing the same in neighbouring parishes and McAlinden was being moved interstate. I hadn't known about Donovan and Quirk. Shaun explained they were dead, but the Diocese had paid compensation to survivors for the crimes committed against them. It set my mind racing. I hadn't thought about deceased clergy. When they were added to the mix, the scandal became bigger.

When Shaun mentioned Philip Wilson, my mind turned to the Fletcher investigation. Shaun, however, wanted to discuss McAlinden. Joanne McCarthy had provided him with documents connecting Bishop Leo Clarke and Bishop Michael Malone, among others, to Denis McAlinden. The documents turned out to be the 1995 statements, and other material, relating to Denise and Anthea, the sisters sexually abused by their uncle, Denis McAlinden.

On 27 April 2010, Joanne published 'Secrets of the Bishops: How Hunter Church leaders failed to report paedophile priest'. It was a watershed story. The Hunter's equivalent to the *Boston Globe* expose of 2002. The documents were damning, disclosing that McAlinden abused a young girl on his lap during confession. It also revealed the Church knew survivors were prepared 'to give testimony under oath'.

It revealed Clarke telling McAlinden, 'Your good name will be protected by the confidential nature of the [Church] process'.

Joanne pointed out, 'This was despite the Church having evidence of the priest's sexual abuse of children over many years'.

Clarke had been trying, with the assistance of Philip Wilson, Brian Lucas and Allan Hart, to defrock McAlinden. That is, they wanted to laicise him, remove him from the clerical state, to stop him being a priest. The procedure was virtually impossible if the priest at the centre of the process didn't consent, and McAlinden didn't consent.

Archbishop Wilson and Father Brian Lucas declined to answer Joanne's questions about their involvement, or why they hadn't reported McAlinden to police.

As Shaun continued, I realised Clarke had been fully aware of McAlinden's abuse of Anthea and Denise. I couldn't be certain, but it was likely these were the women Annette spoke to me about eight years earlier in 2002. Whether or not it was them was immaterial. When I visited Clarke in 2002, he denied any knowledge of McAlinden's victims. Shaun now had proof that Clarke knew of other victims as early as 1995.

I gave Shaun a copy of what I had sent the Ombudsman in 2003, and told him of my interaction with the Diocese and the Ombudsman's refusal to provide me with their report. I then made a call to authorise Shaun to collect the McAlinden and Fletcher files from Maitland Police Station.

With my 2005–06 reports to investigate Church concealment having not been responded to, I told Shaun I was pleased someone was finally looking at the issue. He was keen to start investigating.

Shaun returned the following month, saying O'Hearn had told him, 'I know a good police officer.' Shaun felt O'Hearn mentioned this to improperly influence his investigation. If so, it failed to work. Shaun was above that.

During this meeting, I told Shaun of the incident involving the police prosecutor the day I charged Fletcher and that I'd once been told, 'Beware of the Catholic Mafia'.

I hadn't used the term since hearing it in 2003. I used it now to describe those who might place loyalty to the Church before all else. My one-off utterance of that term would come back to haunt me.

When Shaun mentioned Brian Lucas, I suggested he ring Troy Grant, because Troy had mentioned Lucas and Cotter to me in relation to his investigation of Vince Ryan. Shaun also wanted to speak to witnesses from my Fletcher investigation who might know more about any potential cover-up. I said I would chase them up. Beyond supplying information, I had no intention of becoming any more involved. Shaun was more than capable and I had little doubt he would be assigned help.

In June, I answered a call from Joanne McCarthy. The first since I gave her the brush-off two years earlier when she called me at Newcastle concerning David O'Hearn. Joanne had been speaking to a woman whose name I had heard mentioned during the Fletcher investigation, who I have referred to as Barbara earlier in this story. Barbara had confronted Church authorities about Denis McAlinden seventeen years earlier. Try as she might, Joanne couldn't persuade Barbara to speak with police.

So, what did that have to do with me? Joanne explained that Barbara indicated she was prepared to speak with Peter Fox.

'Why?'

We had never met. It turned out Barbara knew other families of clergy survivors who I had dealt with. Those persons had praised me to Barbara, not knowing she too was a survivor. As a result, Barbara felt she could trust me. Hesitantly, I agreed to speak with her. Any statement, however, would be passed on. I was happy to assist Shaun with files and sharing my knowledge and leave everything in his hands.

•

When I called in early June, Barbara insisted I not come to her home. She didn't want anyone to know of our meeting. When we met soon after the call, Barbara told me everything she had already told Joanne, and Joanne was right – it was significant. That said, Barbara was undecided about providing a statement.

Barbara was articulate, but still dealing with her demons. She feared ostracism, not just for her, but her family too. I knew I had to give her time. We stayed in touch until she made her decision three weeks later.

I started Barbara's statement on 29 June 2010. It took longer than expected, more than a month, as we stopped and started for Barbara to check and double-check. I had typed thousands of statements, but Barbara's will forever stand out. She was particular to the nth degree. As usual, my screen was angled so she could read what I typed. Even so, she took a copy home after each session, returning with the pages marked with pen. Words had to be changed or sentences added. If she recalled something new, it would be written down to be incorporated. It was a lot of work, but I didn't mind. I understood that it was important to record everything to her satisfaction. If ever I had recorded a statement to a person's precise instruction, it was

Barbara's. She even wanted it recorded how long we had taken to type her statement: more than twenty-eight hours. She had timed it.

We documented her childhood abuse and how, as an adult, she confided in Philip Wilson. There was her 1993 complaint to Monsignor Allan Hart, who asked if she wanted it taken further. Hart agreed with Barbara, Denis McAlinden had to be stopped. Then there was the call from Brian Lucas, followed by McAlinden's admissions of sexually abusing others. Barbara described her hurt and anger that Lucas had failed to ask if she had a maiden name. Learning the Church was buying McAlinden a ticket to England and of his plan to return to Australia, Barbara became angry, threatening to go to the media. Angry and frustrated, that's when she walked away from the Church process.

Barbara vented about the Church's failures, particularly its mismanagement and concealment of child sexual abuse. Lucas and Towards Healing were part of the problem, she said. Barbara felt the Church would never change unless change was imposed.

Barbara said that, had Church leaders supported her going to the police, she would have. Her commitment to her Church prevented that happening. Back then Barbara was prepared to make a statement if the Church gave its blessing, she told me. It didn't, so the whole mess was left with the Church and went nowhere. The Church proved itself incapable and reluctant to deal with the issue. If the sexual abuse of children and its concealment were going to be addressed, deferring to the Church needed to stop and police needed to act.

CHAPTER 15

SCURRILOUS ALLEGATIONS

By 2010, scandals in the Hunter Valley started concerning even those as far away as Rome. Cardinal William Levada, in charge of the Congregation for the Doctrine of the Faith, started asking questions about clergy abuse in the region.

•

Detective Inspector Paul Jacob was often jolly, a trait fitting his physique. I got to know Paul in the mid-2000s when he invited me to be a guest presenter at the homicide investigator's course. We shared a few beers and occasionally met for coffee.

In May 2010 lawyers for Adelaide's Archbishop were anxious to know if police were going to investigate the allegations of cover-up against Philip Wilson. They didn't contact Newcastle Police, but instead spoke to Paul Jacob at the Sex Crimes Squad based in Parramatta. Paul made inquiries on their behalf. Paul made inquiries on their behalf before contacting a senior police officer at Charlestown. He then sent an email to another senior police officer at Newcastle. In the email, Paul called the allegations against Archbishop Wilson *scurrilous*.

No abuse survivors or witnesses had yet been spoken to by police when Paul raised Denis McAlinden and Bishop Clarke being dead, before writing: 'Although this inquiry/assessment may have to be handled with diplomacy there is no prospect of any criminal investigation outcomes'.

It wasn't long before Shaun McLeod was told by his superiors to hand over his documents and cease investigating allegations of Church cover-up. When Joanne McCarthy continued to provide Shaun with material, he was called up and told to cease all contact with her.

Shaun wasn't his buoyant self when next we met. 'I'm frustrated no one will investigate this serious criminal cover-up in the Catholic Church,' he told me. 'They are going to do nothing, just review it.' He felt the whole thing was just going to be buried.

I could hear the upset in his voice.

Shaun took sick leave soon after, and never returned.

Concerned about Shaun, Joanne rang me. She had been told by a senior police officer that Wilson wasn't going to be investigated. When she vigorously queried this, the line changed to there might be an investigation.

Joanne's scrutiny was making this a hot potato. The Wilson file was sent from Charlestown to Newcastle, then to the Sex Crimes Squad in Sydney. Barrister Andrew Morrison of the Australian Lawyers Alliance was following events through Joanne McCarthy and called on police to act. There were indications the file would go to the commissioner's executive team, but then it was sent to Northern Region, before the file made its way back to Newcastle. Then it returned to Charlestown. It was enough to make one dizzy, but the hot potato didn't stop there. The investigation made its way back to Region before again being sent to Newcastle. With Joanne looking over their shoulder, it seemed no one wanted anything to do with it. In the seven months police received and then passed the file on, more Hunter clergy came under investigation.

•

Having seen documents obtained by Joanne, I couldn't understand police reluctance. Was I missing something? I had never met McAlinden's nieces, Denise and Anthea. I knew a bit of their story through Joanne's newspaper articles and Barbara's statement. I had seen their documents when shown to me by Shaun. To better understand why police were so reluctant to take on this investigation, I arranged to speak to Anthea and Denise myself. In the meantime I spoke to Helen Keevers, whose position at the Church's Child Protection Unit had been terminated by a council of priests that included Fathers David O'Hearn and Peter Brock, who themselves were allegedly involved in child sexual abuse, as well as Monsignor Allan Hart, who knew of child sexual abuse involving Father McAlinden and failed to report it to police.

Helen was no longer bound by employee confidentiality. I knew about Brian Lucas's role investigating Vince Ryan, Peter Comensoli and Michael Evans, and now it seemed he had investigated but not reported McAliden's admissions of child sexual abuse to police. Helen already knew this.

'And what about Fletcher?'

Helen said that when Fletcher was spoken to at Branxton, the Church had acted on the advice of the Church's Professional Standards Office, which worked hand in glove with Towards

Healing. Despite Towards Healing stipulating nothing should be done to interfere with a police investigation, someone told the Diocese to act to the contrary. Helen was sure of that.

Helen also told me of Encompass Australasia, a controversial Church program treating clergy for paedophilia and other disorders. Files from the program supposedly contained clergy admitting to child sexual abuse. The program never reported any of this to police. After treatment, the program even facilitated the movement of priests like Vince Ryan, who was sent for treatment in Melbourne, to new parishes. Helen said files from the program were hidden in Canberra, and she was worried they might go missing. She suggested simultaneous search warrants be executed in Canberra, the Church Professional Standards office in Sydney and Catholic Church Insurance in Melbourne to ensure police obtained everything. I was amazed by what Helen had learned in her time working for the Diocese. These were astonishing revelations that left me speechless. I couldn't believe senior police weren't grabbing these investigations in both hands and running with them.

In June 2010, as Newcastle Police passed the Church file in never-ending circles and maintained that they weren't in a position to charge anyone, Cardinal George Pell received a letter from the Vatican's Cardinal Levada. Disturbed by international media coverage on the extent of child abuse in the Hunter, particularly the crimes of Father John Denham, Levada wanted to know more. Pell passed inquiries on to Bishop Malone with the remit of the file quickly expanding. Malone was soon putting together information for the Vatican on Denham, Ryan, Fletcher, McAlinden and O'Hearn, including victim payments and how much of those compensation payments was covered by Catholic Church insurance. At the time, I didn't know any of this. I just knew that with the loss of Shaun and wavering commitment from senior police, I had to do more myself. I needed to speak to Anthea and Denise.

•

Anthea and Denise were close. Sure, they were sisters, but their support for each other went beyond being siblings. Neither beat around the bush, which I liked. As I sat evaluating them, I sensed they were doing the same with me. You couldn't blame them. After what they had been through, they had every reason to be wary. And, it wasn't just the Church. Anthea's dealings with police hadn't exactly thrilled her. In April 2010, she had written to a senior police officer, identifying herself as the person who gave Joanne McCarthy the Wilson documents.

'To date the Catholic Church has been able to claim that pedophilia [sic] was a crime limited to the behaviour of a few priests and that there was no conspiracy of silence within the Church. The documents relating to the defrocking of Denis McAlinden proves that this is not the case.'

When I learned what Anthea had written, I was at a loss to understand the lack of police commitment to take this investigation further. Anthea pleaded with the senior officer, 'Please do not ignore my request – I need to know the state of NSW cares about me and other victims, and that the Catholic Church is not treated as a special case when it comes to concealing crimes.'

Soon after, the senior officer sent a report to Region praising Bishop Malone's cooperation and holding Towards Healing up as 'a comprehensive policy and procedure for dealing with abuse allegations'.

It was high praise indeed considering Anthea had asked police not to treat the Church as a special case. I was reluctant to become involved, but could see if this investigation was to have any chance, it need commitment and vigour to drive it.

Because of the trauma Denise and Anthea suffered when the Church tape-recorded their statements, I assured both that their police statements would be typed. Anthea told me her sexual abuse started when she was eight and continued for three or four years, including one crime committed in confession. Denise's ordeal was similar to that of her sister. As Denise had to return interstate, I took her statement first.

She spoke about McAlinden's acquittal in Perth and how it resulted in Anthea and her opening up to one another. Denise remembered every detail of her encounter with Philip Wilson as if it were yesterday. After her experience with the Church, it would take time before she was again ready to trust someone enough to talk about her abuse at the hands of her uncle. It started when Denise was eleven and continued for two years, going well beyond touching. We left it there. She wasn't ready. She planned to return to Newcastle in a few months, and I hoped she would be able to talk about it then.

Denise acknowledged that she was never directly told that the Church was going to take her complaint to police, but from all the formalities she believed that to be its intention.

'We were never offered or encouraged in any way to pursue that avenue separately.'

Swearing on the bible, for Denise, confirmed it was a legal process that would be passed on to police. Her only concern was for their mother, McAlinden's sister.

'I would have been happy for them to inform the police as long as Anthea and I could remain anonymous, so far as Mum was concerned.'

Denise didn't know how the Church would forward her complaint, but she waited for police to call. Neither she nor Anthea were given a copy of their statements, but still, Denise was confident that McAlinden would soon 'be charged or locked up'.

Then, silence. Days turned into weeks, as months became years. There was no pastoral care. Wilson was promoted to Wollongong, and Bishop Leo Clarke retired.

'They did nothing from what I saw and heard. We didn't hear anything. He [McAlinden] was just moved about from place to place where people would not have been aware of his history and he was free to target other children. I just cannot understand how ... the Church could know about the terrible crimes this man committed and not have him brought to justice or pay any penalty.'

Both sisters eventually came to the realisation the Church buried what happened to them.

'I reflected on the way my statement was taken. I believe that it was all tucked away and was only a process to shut Sister Paula, Anthea and I up. We kept expecting something to happen and as time went by it died a natural death.'

A decade later, Denise learned that her uncle had admitted to another priest that he had abused her.

'Surely, whoever he admitted molesting me to could have taken this to the police and given that evidence in court.' She was not aware Brian Lucas, the priest who obtained McAlinden's admission of abuse, had a policy of not taking notes or that the Church did not report admissions to police.

'If I had been told in 1995 that he had admitted to molesting me I would have insisted the matter be reported to the police. I would not have hesitated. I would not have had to think about it. I know I might have had to give evidence at court, but I would have asked for my name to be suppressed. I would have risked that. If he did admit to another priest that he sexually abused me, it would be hard for him to get off it even if he pleaded not guilty later. What was he going to say, "That the other priest made that up and was lying"? In all likelihood, he probably would have pleaded guilty and been sent to gaol where he belonged.'

Denise's statement was explosive. Her evidence showed how the Church concealed its crimes. Before Denise left, I annexed a copy of the statement and legal documents the Church had her sign. Anthea and Denise obtained those documents after Wilson refused to meet and conciliate with Anthea in 2008.

Helen Keevers worked closely with Bishop Malone. She could be persuasive and no doubt was a positive influence on him. Malone would later say he had an 'epiphany'. Which is when Helen said his attitude to the way the Church dealt with child sexual abuse had changed. The point is, this is when Helen had Malone agree to her providing the Church documents obtained by Wilson to Anthea and Denise as part of the conciliation process.

I assured Denise I would not repeat the abandonment she had experienced with the Church. I would keep in touch. I would type Anthea's statement when I returned from holidays.

There was something in Denise's statement to the Church that bothered me. Something I couldn't put my finger on. Like I'd read it before. Perhaps I was wrong. Maybe I was remembering something else. I went home disconcerted.

Sister Paula Redgrove, the nun who Anthea had confided in, agreed to speak with me. When I obtained a statement from Mike Stanwell, the former Merriwa school principal who had tried to have Wilson and Bishop Clarke act on Denis McAlinden back in 1986, I was confident the investigation was going places. That said, what happened to Shaun still troubled me. I decided to involve myself further to ensure the investigation was conducted properly.

The day before I went on leave, I received a file from the police minister's office, about 'possible cover-up of the crimes of paedophile priests by senior people within the Catholic Church'.

A Hunter abuse survivor's sibling had written to the minister about senior Church officials concealing child abuse: 'I do not know anything about Father McAlinden or Father Denham, but I do have a lot of experience of Father Fletcher.' After the file left the minister's office, someone noticed I had been in charge of the investigation into Fletcher. They attached to the file an intelligence report I submitted in 2004 concerning Church cover-up. The file was then sent to me.

I believed that in receiving the file I was on the right track in investigating these crimes, with the minister's office raising Section 316, the crime of concealing a serious offence.

•

While I was talking to Anthea, Denise and others, the police file concerning Church concealment of child sexual abuse, which had been bouncing between police commands, found its way back to Newcastle. Kirren Steel had been recruited from uniform duties to take over Shaun's investigation. I got to know Kirren and her cheerful disposition during my stay at Newcastle. She had once worked as a detective before opting to return to general duties. Drafted back into the detectives' office, Kirren was handed the Catholic Church investigation. I still don't understand why the investigation was taken from Shaun to be given to someone lacking recent experience in child abuse investigations.

Before I started leave, I rang Kirren. When there was no answer, I sent an email telling her about the ministerial file, witness statements I had obtained and my previous involvement with McAlinden. I suggested we sit down when I returned from leave. I didn't want any suggestions of failing to notify the chain of command, so I copied in senior police at Region.

I still felt the need to be cautious. Years earlier, an inspector's office was illegally searched and statements disappeared, which I will talk more about shortly. I didn't want to see something similar repeated here. I took the unusual step of securing the ministerial file and everything else in my office safe. With one key and a broken handle I thought the safe was dumped in my office just to get it out of the way. It weighed a ton, but still worked, so I now put it to good use.

CHAPTER 16

THE SECRET SEARCH

When I returned from leave in mid-October 2010, a worried work colleague spoke to me. This person relayed seeing two senior police officers entering my office and searching it from top to bottom for a brief relating to the Catholic Church. The colleague then told me, 'I didn't think what they were doing looked right.'

Learning of this I felt my jaw drop and the blood drain from my face. I sat with my door closed, feeling suddenly sick to my stomach and unsure what to do. I had never heard of a senior officer's room being searched in such a manner. The exception was an illegal search of an inspector's office at Singleton where certain sexual abuse investigation statements mysteriously disappeared. I knew an internal investigation had followed. The missing statements weren't found and the person responsible was never identified.

Things in my office had been moved and I observed that someone had definitely rifled through my files. I pulled the key out of my pocket – the one I had taken home while I was on leave – and opened the safe. Everything was still there.

I decided to say nothing. If the search was legitimate, I would be told. Despite me later speaking to those officers, neither volunteered anything about searching my office.

From past events I knew searches of that nature weren't normal. About 2003 rumours emanated out of Nelson Bay surrounding Probationary Constable Luke Tink. Tink struck me as a real ladies' man who loved the image of himself in uniform. When a schoolgirl complained that Tink indecently assaulted her in a police car, a senior officer spoke with the girl and her mother following which I was told the girl's complaint was withdrawn.

Allegations against Tink didn't stop, with the next complaint allocated to an officer from Singleton to investigate. This inspector soon realised it wasn't Tink's first complaint. Tink's sexual predation had been going on for years. As the scale of his crimes became clear, a disturbing pattern emerged. Tink had a fetish for young girls, most of whom were aged fifteen or younger. Ephebophilia bordering on paedophilia. Some crimes predated Tink's application to join the police force. His uniform and police car just made targeting victims easier. How a probationary constable was able to cruise around alone at night in a police car was never explained. Girls were lured into the car and driven to dirt tracks, deserted beach car parks or bush tracks, where Tink assaulted them.

One victim disclosed the names of girls at her school whom Tink had targeted, who in turn disclosed others. As the brief grew, more than a dozen girls came forward, some prepared to give evidence, others too frightened.

The police station was abuzz as rumours of threats against the investigating officer began to circulate. I don't know if any of it is true, but I did notice that the investigating inspector didn't look well when he took leave, with Tink's brief locked in his office. That's when the statements disappeared. The inspector went to Professional Standards, only to be disappointed. He never saw the matter finalised, leaving the police force as his health deteriorated.

If the full story was exposed, I was sure the loss of public confidence would be scandalous. Luke Tink was charged with thirty-eight offences including kidnap, rape and aggravated indecent assault of children. For reasons that remain unclear, the more serious charges of kidnap and rape were withdrawn as the thirty-eight offences were whittled down to seven.

The case dragged on for four years, with Judge Deborah Payne noting a very long internal investigation was conducted. Shrewd bargaining by Tink's lawyers resulted in him pleading guilty to the seven lesser charges. Passing sentence in 2007, Judge Payne was left in the dark, although she appeared to sense something wasn't right. 'It must be said the gross delay in this case after committal is, in my experience, unusual ... The issue is a troubling one, it seems, with no clear explanation forthcoming apart from the delay being neither Tink's nor the Crown's fault.'

The police force said nothing. Judge Payne noted that certain offences that occurred when Tink was a police officer didn't proceed, saying 'In my view it was most generous and ill-conceived for the Crown not to rely on this.'

Had those offences proceeded you would have to wonder what might have been revealed. This was how the NSW Police Force dealt with a child sexual abuse scandal within its own ranks. Now my office had been searched for a brief concerning concealment of child sexual abuse within the Catholic Church. I was worried. I knew how misplaced loyalties could lead to procedural missteps or worse.

•

On the day I returned from leave in late 2010, I was asked about the file I had received from the minister's office about the *possible cover-up of clergy child sexual abuse within the Maitland–Newcastle Diocese of the Catholic Church.* A decision had been made, I was told, for it to be investigated by police at Newcastle. I was ordered to surrender the file I had locked in my safe. My blood boiled. I argued that the allegations occurred in Maitland, not Newcastle. I knew people named in the file, and yet I wasn't consulted. I tried to remain calm. Police at Newcastle had never been involved with Fletcher. Why did the senior officer making this decision think the file was sent to me in the first place? There was no response. I now understood how Shaun felt when told to surrender the McAlinden documents. I demanded to know who made this decision, but I wasn't given an answer. This was an opportunity for this officer to tell me about the search of my office, but nothing was said.

The next morning I sent the file off as instructed with a covering report offering statements and other evidence. That evidence included my knowledge of Bishop Clarke's failure to disclose to me his knowledge about Anthea, Denise, Barbara and other McAlinden victims when I spoke to Clarke in 2002. There was also evidence provided by Adam's and Daniel Feenan's families. Before the file arrived at Newcastle, I received an abrasive phone call demanding the file. Explaining it was on its way, I began to offer some background on Fletcher. It was rejected.

My offer of assistance was never taken up, and the person who wrote to the minister alleging a Church cover-up of James Fletcher's crimes would not be spoken to for nearly a year. So, why the urgency to relieve me of the file? I now feared it was only a matter of time before the McAlinden statements, including those I took from Denise, Barbara and former Merriwa school principal, Mike Stanwell, were also demanded.

When I next phoned Anthea she told me Denise was planning to visit over Christmas and would get back to me with dates to finish their statements.

After a failed attempt to speak with those at Region, I submitted a report. In the narrative I included information about the concealment of Vince Ryan's crimes by Monsignor Patrick Cotter and the DPP's decision not to prosecute him. I also raised the interference I experienced from Church officials during the Fletcher investigation. Unknown to me at this time, Fletcher survivor Peter Gogarty had sent a senior police officer a letter earlier in 2010 concerning his perpetrator, offering information about 'the systemic cover-up of the crimes of paedophile priests in the Hunter Valley'.

In my report, I used excerpts from Denise's statement, particularly her expectation of the Church going to police, before I recorded my view that, 'There is sufficient evidence to conduct a full and comprehensive investigation into the conduct of the Maitland–Newcastle Diocese of the Catholic Church. There is more than enough evidence to put before the Attorney-General under section 316 of the *Crimes Act* to prosecute a number of clergy based on evidence already cited.'

However, it seemed those in power took a different view, with a senior officer weighing up the pros and cons of prosecuting clergy in his report to the Region Commander: 'It would appear that the manner in which the Catholic Church deals with these matters has substantially changed since 1995. This includes the "Towards Healing" process and procedure, Bishop Malone's cooperation with Strike Force Georgiana and his involvement in Zimmerman House. The fact alleged offenders were in fact actually taking steps to remove him [McAlinden] from the

Church could also be seen as a mitigating factor. Investigating and prosecuting persons with this background and in these circumstances could potentially bring the law into disrepute. It also appears that the victim's attitude in 1995 was that the matter should not be reported to police. This obviously needs to be clarified. In these circumstances an investigation and/or prosecution could be seen as harsh and oppressive ... Finally the availability of an alternate to the criminal process via the "Towards Healing" process would mitigate against embarking on this course of action.'

The promotion of the Church's Towards Healing protocol as an alternative to criminal justice and suggesting an investigation could be seen as harsh and oppressive aside, where did the belief that Denise didn't want the Church to go to police come from? For this to hold true, Denise's statement would have to disappear together with my report quoting her preparedness to go to police. I didn't want anything to go missing, and after the search of my office, I was more than a little apprehensive. My past experience of questionable police conduct filled me with trepidation.

CHAPTER 17

BLIND REPORTING

As the *Boston Globe* began reporting in 2002, demands grew for the Boston Archdiocese to turn over the names of all priests accused of child sexual abuse. Under ever-increasing pressure, Cardinal Bernard Law yielded. It didn't take long, however, for prosecutors to realise that what Church officials provided was useless. While paedophile priest names were passed on, the Church withheld the names of victims. Without victim names, cases could not be investigated.

The Archdiocese continued ignoring prosecutors' requests for the missing material to be turned over – that is, until five district attorneys banded together. In a combined letter, they intimated that if the files weren't forthcoming, Church leaders could be dragged before grand juries. Within twenty-four hours Cardinal Law relented, turning over the names of victims. Some trials resulted, though US statute-of-limitation laws prevented many priests from being prosecuted. I could never have imagined that the Catholic Church in NSW, with police assistance, was employing a similar tactic.

•

The Catholic Church provided more intelligence to police about Denis McAlinden after his death in 2005 than was received in all the years he was alive. In fact, the Church wasn't just passing on information solely on McAlinden, but on dozens, if not hundreds, of suspected paedophile clergy. The Catholic Church was passing on reports directly to the Sex Crimes Squad in Sydney. The seven reports I examined concerning McAlinden detailed McAlinden's rape and sexual abuse of no fewer than fifteen girls, the youngest aged only four. There was no mention of when the Church first became aware of these crimes, nor were NSW Police asking. Reading the reports, it was evident to me that the information wasn't new. I recognised details in two of the reports. I knew survivors had complained to the Church many years before the Church reported them to police.

As in Boston, the Church knew who the victims were but weren't providing their names, so none of the crimes in NSW could be investigated. In contrast to US authorities, NSW Police weren't demanding the Church hand over victim's names. I would soon discover NSW Police had set up a reporting system exclusively for the Catholic Church, even drafting official forms to facilitate the smooth running of the process. I found myself asking if this was legal. In New South Wales, under s316 of the *Crimes Act*, reporting child sexual abuse was mandatory (with exceptions for various professions, such as ministers of religion, about which I will say more shortly). So, why was the Church allowed to pick and choose what information it passed on?

When I first came across the McAlinden intelligence reports supplied after his death, I was mystified. Telephoning the Sex Crimes Squad, I learned the process was called 'blind reporting'. I had never heard of it, and, dare I say, nor had most police.

Questioning why the rape of children was being recorded as 'intelligence only' instead of a crime, I was told there wasn't enough information to do otherwise. The dates, locations and graphic details of child sexual abuse in the McAlinden reports left nothing to the imagination. After reading a couple of the reports to the officer on the other end of the phone, I asked again. There was a pause before the officer told me she was only doing as instructed. Under an exclusive arrangement between NSW Police and the Catholic Church, hundreds, if not thousands, of similar reports were being processed.

So how did such a process come into being?

Nicholas Tonti-Filippini was a leading authority in the little-known field of bioethics, the study of ethical dilemmas resulting from the advancement of medicine and biology. As early as 1990, soon after Brian Lucas returned from his first trip to the United States, Tonti-Filippini loaned his expertise to the Catholic Church. He wrote to Lucas expressing grave reservations about a draft child sexual abuse protocol. Tonti-Filippini viewed it as an attempt to circumvent mandatory reporting laws and warned Lucas against placing the Church's reputation ahead of protecting children.

After giving evidence about the Wollongong scandal and his involvement with Father Comensoli and Brother Evans to the Police Royal Commission in 1996, Lucas spoke publicly about the Church's child abuse policy. What Lucas said so alarmed Tonti-Filippini that he felt compelled to write to Bishop Kevin Manning. Lucas, he said, was exploiting the legal exemption for ministers of religion to report child sexual abuse. Legal privilege exempted doctors, lawyers and the like from disclosing confidential information. In New South Wales Lucas successfully lobbied for ministers of religion to be part of that privileged group, exempting them from mandatory reporting of child sexual abuse under s316. Tonti-Filippini warned the exception was only 'intended to protect the sacred seal of the confessional'.

Lucas, it seemed, was applying the law more broadly to include admissions outside the confessional, such as those Lucas had obtained from McAlinden.

Tonti-Filippini believed if this broad interpretation and Lucas's conduct was exposed the fallout would end the legal protection of the confessional. As for the policy of not telling police and keeping child sexual abuse investigations in-house, Tonti-Filippini was scathing: 'Sooner or later the matter will be exposed and the serious mistake of continuing to have these matters handled by clergy alone will cause great damage to the Church, especially the allegations of subterfuge.'

Pushing Tonti-Filippini's concerns aside, Sydney's Cardinal Edward Clancy wrote to the police commissioner proposing collaboration between NSW Police and Catholic Church authorities in responding to clergy child sexual abuse. His Eminence appointed Brian Lucas as the NSW Police liaison tasked with establishing an agreement through the Child Protection Enforcement Agency (CPEA), forerunner of the Sex Crimes Squad. A draft Memorandum of Understanding (MOU) was completed by June 1997, stating that when a complainant was absent but a person was suspected of committing an offence against a child, 'the Church will be able to report the matter to the CPEA for "intelligence purposes only"'.

For the Church, any MOU had to work hand in glove with Towards Healing.

When one police officer, Sergeant Carolyn O'Hare, read Towards Healing in conjunction with the MOU, she started asking awkward questions.

'Did the protocol comply with legal responsibilities and obligations?'

'Did it conform to the Child Care and Protection Act?'

'Did they (the Catholic Church) realise interviewing victims might jeopardise police investigations?'

All valid questions, but perhaps the most important was: 'Where an accused is interviewed and an admission is made, are there any occasions when that admission will be made available to the police?'

With the Church's policy of not reporting child sexual abuse to police, the last question must have been disconcerting. For whatever reason, the MOU wasn't signed by the police commissioner, however, officers within the CPEA continued collaborating with the Church as if it had been signed.

ABC-TV journalist Suzie Smith would later expose that the police collaboration extended to providing a police officer on the board of the Catholic Church's Professional Standards Resource Group (PSRG). On police time and salary, the officer assisted the Catholic Church to assess child sexual abuse within its ranks. With priests not disclosing anything from the confessional it should have been obvious that cases coming before the board – which included at least one allegation of rape and a child being born to a former priest – should not have been afforded legal protection. At each meeting's end, documents of potential evidence were destroyed, all with police knowledge.

Although victim names were not provided, a 1999 PSRG meeting recorded the passing on of other information to police for 'intelligence purposes', saying it was 'seen to meet the requirements of s316 of the NSW *Crimes Act*'.

Even if police argue they were naive, the Church knew what it was doing. At the bottom of each report made to police, the Church included, 'in accordance with s316 of the NSW *Crimes Act*'.

When initial Church lobbying failed, another attempt was made to recognise the MOU by having it signed by the police commissioner. Sergeant Allan Treadwell of Crime Agencies Legal Support reviewed the document in 2001. It didn't take him long to warn that the proposed MOU would conflict with the law. He said the Act 'requires disclosure of "all" information that might be [of] material assistance in the investigation of a serious indictable offence ... Of course, the name of the person against whom it is said a serious indictable offence has been committed is almost certainly going to be of material assistance in any investigation.'

Treadwell challenged the Church's withholding of victims' names, even when survivors supposedly didn't want police notified.

However, the MOU went further, reserving the Church's right to withhold any information that might reveal an abuse survivor's name. The Church was the sole arbitrator on what was provided. Treadwell pointed out that Church personnel who failed to disclose everything were committing a crime. Passing information on to police might breach confidence, he said, but the failure to provide all information to avoid such a breach was unlikely to be viewed, at law, as a reasonable excuse. Treadwell concluded that private agreements between NSW Police and the Catholic Church were undesirable when such agreements conflicted with the law.

In May 2002, two lawyers from the Police Commercial Law Section joined Treadwell in opposing the MOU, saying the whole process was illegal. The Sex Crimes Squad ignored all this advice, allowing the Church a strong voice in drafting police policy. While Boston's district attorneys threatened to haul Church leaders before grand juries, NSW Police assisted the Church in withholding such information.

Concern about Church protocols wasn't just confined to certain police and lawyers. Within the Church, Tonti-Filippini was still trying to get someone to listen. Joined by a legal advisor, he expressed consternation over what he believed to be a manipulation of the law. In June 2002, Tonti-Filippini wrote to Archbishop George Pell, who had relocated to Sydney following the death of Archbishop Edward Clancy: 'The principal objective of the [Church's] policy [was] to avoid scandal for all concerned and prevent further harm to victims and accused by avoiding public exposure'.

Tonti-Filippini felt powerless as the Church seemed primarily focused on damage control.

Tonti-Filippini also wrote to Bishop Ronald Mulkearns in Ballarat, mentioning 'misprision' to describe 'the policy of relying on investigation exclusively by priests and the legal privilege of the confessional to prevent crime becoming known to the civil authorities'.

Tonti-Filippini even wrote to the Apostolic Nuncio, the Vatican's Australian ambassador, telling him the damage was being compounded by bishops not reporting child abuse: 'Bishops and religious superiors may also have been guilty of misprision in the more serious sense in that they deliberately, actively concealed crime.'

He described what was going on as 'a clerical conspiracy to commit misprision'.

Despite all these warnings, collaboration between the Catholic Church and NSW Police continued.

•

I had spoken to Michael McDonald of the Catholic Commission for Employment Relations a number of times during my investigation of James Fletcher, before I complained to the Ombudsman in March 2003. That complaint related to the Church's failure to notify the Ombudsman of the allegations against Fletcher and have him removed from contact with children. As the Ombudsman began to investigate McDonald and the Church's Professional Standards Office for having not stood Fletcher down, McDonald wasted no time contacting the officer in charge of the Sex Crimes Squad, Superintendent Kim McKay.

McDonald told her, 'You will appreciate the difficulty in standing a person down from child-related employment before charges are laid,' before he desperately sought 'confirmation that the unsigned Memorandum of Understanding with the police remains in place'.

Concerned by the unsigned MOU protocols apparently being acted upon, McKay sought legal advice from Police Legal Services, who told McKay the MOU had not been approved and should not have been directing police relationships with the Church. A third lawyer now joined Treadwell and the two lawyers mentioned earlier in re-stating that the MOU was 'inconsistent with the law'.

McKay had apparently been kept out of the loop, with some police choosing to ignore the earlier legal advice. Brought up to speed, McKay now told McDonald that the MOU was illegal – specifically, the Church's failure to report all knowledge of a serious crime. The Church, it seemed, was now out in the cold.

In addition to Treadwell saying the withholding of victims' names and other information was incongruent with the law, blind reporting also conflicted with police policy. 'If *information obtained describes an* **offence** *a* COPS Event [Crime Report] **must** *be submitted. An IR* [Intelligence Report] *is not a substitute for a COPS Event.'*

Despite this, the Catholic Church continued withholding victim's names whilst the Sex Crimes Squad continued to record clergy child sexual abuse as intelligence only.

Unlike 'events', 'intelligence reports' weren't permanent. After specified periods, intelligence is designed to be removed, disappearing from the police system altogether. Not only that, intelligence is not counted as a crime, not by police and not by departments such as the Bureau of Crime Statistics. Half a dozen sexual assaults at universities or childcare facilities would raise a red flag, whereas hundreds, if not thousands of reports of child sexual abuse within the Catholic Church would statistically go unnoticed. They simply didn't appear. No one would ask what was being done because no one would know. Intended or not, the result was alarming numbers of child sexual assaults went unnoticed by everyone but the victims.

What was to be gained by the Church belatedly reporting all this to NSW Police? I don't know. Some might suggest that blind reporting unscrupulously fulfilled the Church's legal obligation to report child sexual abuse under s316, while at the same time avoiding statistical scrutiny and investigation.

The Church and NSW Police supported blind reporting, arguing that abuse survivors didn't want their matters taken to police. But how did police know this when all they had was the word of the offending institution? Later police evidence to the Police Integrity Commission acknowledged that police had no way of knowing, outside of what the Church told them.

•

Perturbed by the whole process, I went back through the blind-reported intelligence on Denis McAlinden. I must have read the reports three or four times before it struck. Suddenly I held in my hand the answer to the question that had troubled me about Denise's statement. Grabbing her Church statement, I read it again. There it was, nearly word for word, they were identical. The Church blind-reported Denise's abuse. It was a charade. Denise hadn't told the Church not to report her abuse to police. She wanted action, yet here it was under the pretext she didn't want police involved. With her Church statement having been typed in 1995, it wasn't reported until 2009, fourteen years after the Church learned of her abuse and well after McAlinden's death. It had laid hidden within the Church for more than a decade. I had stumbled across this one, but how many more like it were hidden among the thousands of other blind reports?

CHAPTER 18

STRIKEFARCE

Thursday, 2 December 2010 turned out to be the day I had been dreading. That's when I was instructed to attend a meeting in Newcastle later that morning and bring any documents involving the Catholic Church. I was told the Crime Agencies Sex Crimes Squad would be there to discuss the scale and scope of any future investigation. Cursing the late notice, I hurriedly cancelled other appointments.

Superintendent Max Mitchell chaired the meeting at Waratah Police Station.

Superintendent Charlie Haggett was there to represent our command's interests. When I arrived, he was already in conversation with Max. Other officers were there as well, but no one from the Sex Crimes Squad. One of the officers at the meeting had only called me the day before to inquire about the statements I had obtained.

Even before I sat down, one officer demanded the statements. When I told them I'd forgotten to grab them, they told me that I'd been directed to bring them.

'I don't need them here,' I said. 'I know what they contain.'

I was told in no uncertain terms that it wasn't my investigation.

I would later tell the Cunneen Inquiry the meeting was more an inquisition. The mere mention of Joanne McCarthy's name sparked hostility. I pointed out that Joanne had started the investigation by providing information and documents. Victims trusted her more than they did police. It was well established that using the media encouraged victims to come forward and I believed Joanne had a lot more information. I argued for Joanne to be brought on board, even suggesting she sign a confidentiality agreement.

I was told that's not how we operate.

Communication with Joanne McCarthy was to cease. From here on, Strike Force Lantle, which came into existence some months earlier when Kirren Steel was recruited from uniform, was to be highly protected – which meant no publicity. This went against established good practice for investigations of this nature. Experience had shown me that the more people who were encouraged to come forward through the media, the stronger a brief got.

Denis McAlinden had abused Annette in Raymond Terrace, not Newcastle. I was the only person in the room with any involvement in his investigation and was already based in Raymond Terrace. I explained how Bishop Clarke had lied to me about Denise and Anthea, the very people now central to this investigation. When I spoke about the links between paedophile priests and urged my colleagues not to confine the investigation to McAlinden, no interest was demonstrated. According to Max, the Region Commander, Carlene York had decreed that McAlinden would be the focus.

Max wasted no time directing I hand over all the statements. And, he wanted them that day. Brad would run the investigation with Justin Quinn and Kirren Steel. From here on, I was to have no further role in any Church investigation. I was halfway through Denise's statement and Anthea was ready to give me hers. Now I was being told to walk away from them, abandon them at this crucial time. No reason was given for this decision, but it was final. I didn't know then that the rumour that I had leaked information to Joanne McCarthy in 2008 had continued to be spread. Her information on O'Hearn came from a Church press release. Was the falsehood that I leaked the information used to exclude me from the investigation? If so, I was never told. All I knew was, having built trust with these survivors, I was stunned. Victims weren't supposed to be treated like commodities and passed from one investigator to another, but I was told to hand everything over and that I should not interfere or contact any of the witnesses again.

Infuriated I said, 'I have to call them to let them know what is going on. I am not prepared to treat them like dirt and just cut them off. These people have been hurt enough.'

Eventually I was permitted to make a single call to each, explaining that another officer was taking over.

I continued pleading for the investigation not to be confined, telling the assembly that Helen Keevers had information on further cover-ups and hidden documents. The role of the Diocese needed to be examined fully. Archbishop Philip Wilson needed to be investigated with regard to Fletcher. Everything I said seemed to be ignored.

The whole thing was anomalous, and I wanted it recorded, so when I returned to my office I diarised the meeting. One of the senior officers at the meeting later told me he thought Newcastle had more resources and staff. I nearly laughed. Everyone knew Newcastle had serious staffing issues.

My next step was to phone survivors, to advise them of the changes and apologise for ceasing my involvement. Asked why I was no longer allowed to be involved or to contact them, I couldn't explain, I didn't know myself. It was even more difficult explaining that I could no longer contact them. I could hear their confusion. After their abandonment by the Church, I felt I was deserting them as well. Even so, there was nothing I could do. In a hierarchical organisation like the police force, I had no choice but to do as directed.

Tony Townsend was an inspector within the Region office, he maintained a close rapport with all the major players. It is not protocol to just walk in and sit down for a meeting with an assistant commissioner, so I asked Tony if he could arrange for me to meet with her, but he told me it was inadvisable, because there was no chance of my being involved in the investigation. It also quashed any prospect that Assistant Commissioner Carlene York, a former prosecutor and newly appointed Region Commander, would learn that the rumour I had leaked information to Joanne was untrue, as was any assertion that I had failed to provide material despite 'numerous requests'.

I wanted to explain my interaction with Joanne McCarthy and interest in the Church. It was no use. The whispers had built a wall. Like Kim McKay, at the Sex Crimes Squad, it seemed Carlene York was being kept out of the loop.

•

Anthea's daughter and son-in-law were both police officers. On 10 December 2010, a week after I was removed from the Church investigation, Anthea's son-in-law phoned me. We had never spoken prior. He told me Anthea was suffering depression after her treatment by officers attached to Strike Force Lantle. He couldn't understand why I was no longer involved. I didn't feel I should say too much, but assured him I would make some phone calls. I called Detective Inspector Graham Parker, who had been a probationary constable at Kurri Kurri when I was a detective at Cessnock. He was now temporarily in the Region office, but he didn't seem especially interested in Anthea's distress.

I next received a call from Anthea herself. She knew I was no longer permitted to talk with her, but she needed help. Hearing Anthea's distress, I couldn't turn her away. Her voice quivered as she explained how she had been treated by Lantle. According to Anthea, Kirren was no longer at work, and now Anthea felt she wasn't being asked for her statement, it was being demanded. Despite explaining she wasn't yet up to it, specific police refused to take no for an answer. Anthea had family commitments with her elderly mother before Christmas but these were brushed aside; she had to do it now. Anthea used 'harassing' and 'intimidate' to describe what was happening. There was no empathy, no compassion. She again felt the same way she had all those years ago before the Church.

Anthea said she now wanted nothing to do with Newcastle police, adding that Lantle was no different to the Church. She pleaded for me to take her statement. As much as I wanted to help, I explained it wouldn't be allowed. I had been directed not to become involved. Anthea broke into tears saying she would tell them it was her idea, it was what she wanted. She would refuse to give a statement to anyone but me. I suspected that others would suggest I had put her up to it. We shouldn't have even been talking. All this would only provide an excuse to jump on me harder. I begged Anthea to try to work with Lantle.

After calming Anthea down, I advised her to write to senior police, politely but firmly, saying she would not provide a statement until the new year. I emphasised it had to be in writing and to keep a copy. If her wishes weren't respected, she could lodge a complaint. I spent a lot of time persuading Anthea to keep trying to work with Lantle. Eventually she agreed, albeit reluctantly.

I had genuinely tried to extricate myself from all contact with witnesses, however, Anthea's call was followed by one from Helen Keevers. Helen told me she had started her statement with Kirren Steel, spending hours discussing cover-ups and the Church's hidden documents, when Kirren purportedly exclaimed, 'This will bring the whole Catholic Church down.'

Helen didn't finish her statement that day, they ran out of time. It was supposed to be completed later. The next day Kirren went home distressed and never returned to work.

When Kirren went on sick report it was common knowledge that Newcastle's detectives were already desperately short of investigators. Days later, Brad Tayler packed up and also walked out the door. Justin Quinn had been on leave since the December meeting and now he too went off on sick leave. In an astonishing collapse of dominos, Strike Force Lantle had lost all three investigators in the space of a week. On 22 December 2010, Dan Proudman at the *Newcastle Herald* wrote, 'One in six Newcastle police officers are on long-term sick leave, including more than half of the city's senior management team and its two highest-ranking investigators.'

Those figures included many in the detectives' office, with the police commissioner asking for answers.

The following day, Joanne McCarthy ran her next story, 'Strikefarce'. She hadn't endeared herself to Newcastle police, and now I imagined they would be seething. Joanne reported that Lantle had 'a name but no detectives', and quoted Max Mitchell as saying, 'Sick-leave applications from Detectives Tayler and Quinn were not unexpected.'

When I read that quote, I was stunned. Why would Max replace me with detectives whose sick leave was not unexpected? The article mentioned Kirren Steel obtaining particularly significant information from a key witness. It turned out that Helen, frustrated at Lantle's inactivity, had spoken to Joanne, leaving more questions than answers.

Hearing that Newcastle's staffing crisis had worsened, I rang the Region office, but my calls weren't returned. I persisted until told that despite staffing problems, I would not be returned to the Church investigation.

Not long after this, Lantle's terms of reference were narrowed, confining the investigation to Denis McAlinden to between 1985 and 1999. It excluded the years when Anthea, Denise, Barbara and three other known survivors were abused. It excluded Bishops Gleeson and Toohey, not to mention the concealment of McAlinden's crimes at Forster, where Helen Keevers mentioned documents had detailed McAlinden's abuse of 'the little ones'.

To me this wasn't mission-creep, but mission-reduction.

•

After uniform duties, Jeff Little worked a few years in plain clothes, mainly specialist units and investigating drug crime. He resigned from the NSW Police Force in 2002 before rejoining in 2007 with the rank of senior constable. Jeff came to Raymond Terrace in uniform where his computer-programming skills were prized. In 2010, Jeff applied for a detective sergeant position at Newcastle. With little general detective work under his belt, Jeff approached me to roster him in my detectives' office. He still had a lot to learn, but benefitted from the experience.

Jeff won the Newcastle position, starting just before the New Year. Like Kirren Steel, he wasn't given time to settle in or acquaint himself with his new role. The minute Jeff walked in the door, he was placed in charge of Lantle. It wasn't Jeff's fault, but you have to ask why. Senior police would later assert Jeff was a highly experienced and qualified investigator. Kirren had also been recruited straight from uniform. Now Jeff, a uniform officer a week earlier, was to cut his teeth on this high-profile and complex investigation.

The NSW Police Force regularly creates strike forces with strange computer-generated names like Lantle. Sometimes they are well staffed; other times they are little more than a name. The public is always given assurances about the progress of strike forces, conjuring up images of dedicated teams of detectives working full-time on an investigation. In reality, they often consist of one or two police giving attention to a job between other cases. Lantle was no different. In a command struggling for staff, Jeff would have had his hands full with other crimes and the daily chores of running an office. I know, I had been there myself. The Church investigation would have to wait.

CHAPTER 19

STRIKE FORCE LANTLE

It had been a year since Joanne McCarthy provided her documents to police, yet by April 2011, Strike Force Lantle had made little progress. Senior police didn't want to acknowledge this, of course. Assistant Commissioner York defended Lantle: 'This is a serious and complex matter currently under investigation and, as such, no comment can be made.'

Truth was, no comment could be made because little had been happening.

Retired Assistant Police Commissioner John Ure said in the *Newcastle Herald* that the investigation was struggling. In the same article, Barrister Andrew Morrison disclosed that in 2010 he had written to Superintendent Max Mitchell questioning police commitment and asking, 'What is it about the Catholic Church that puts it above the law?'

Now, in 2011, Morrison called the police handling a disgrace, adding: 'It seems to me there has been a failure by the police force to pursue very serious issues despite regularly having it drawn to their attention.'

The same newspaper article quoted a Hunter clergy abuse survivor saying police were 'as bad as the church if they failed to investigate the alleged cover-up of an alleged criminal'.

When Chief Inspector Brad Taylor took sick leave back in December, he was replaced by Chief Inspector Wayne Humphrey. Lantle now underwent its third managerial change in four months when Wayne was replaced by Inspector Graham Parker.

Pleasantries during an early phone call between Graham and Joanne McCarthy ended the moment he hung up. In his notes following the call, Graham described Joanne as 'ruthless', someone who would place her job ahead of the interests of victims. He recorded Joanne saying that past investigators lacked 'the interest or desire to pursue this matter with the vigour required'.

He also documented Joanne telling him that previous investigators sounded her out about dropping the case altogether, believing it 'too hard or simply unwinnable'.

Graham's notes spoke louder than his pleasantries over the phone: 'It is difficult to say why DCI Fox would wish to be in charge of this investigation given that most experienced investigators would quickly identify it as one which would fall into the category of "undesirable". The likelihood of obtaining an outcome satisfactory to all, or for that matter any, of the parties involved is highly unlikely.'

All I hear in this is the same negativity that had permeated Lantle since its inception.

Carlene York's statement and Graham's assurances to Joanne didn't hide Lantle's lack of progress. Joanne ran her story on 17 April 2011, 'Inquiry into church cover-up "disgrace"'. Joanne cited a liturgy of failures and delays, leaving certain police ropable. However, charming police wasn't her job. Journalists aren't supposed to give police blind praise. Their responsibility is to report facts. Of course, many police didn't see it that way, and resentment towards Joanne McCarthy grew.

Had it not been for Joanne's constant prodding, one has to wonder if the investigation would have died altogether.

Finally prodded into movement, Lantle called Anthea for her statement – not typed, but electronically recorded. Excuses were made to justify electronically interviewing Anthea, placing other concerns, like recording her precise words above her welfare. I didn't buy it. I had typed dozens, if not hundreds of sexual abuse statements, those of Barbara and Denise included. Not once did I conduct an ERISP interview with an abuse survivor. Anthea had been prepared for me to type her statement. Instead, police now used the same method Wilson employed to traumatise Anthea and Denise all those years ago. It was either insensitive, ignorant or worse. An ERISP doesn't flow like a statement where an abuse survivor can control what's being typed. Instead, it's a question-and-answer process usually reserved for criminals. The acronym says it all: Electronic Recorded Interview with Suspected Person. Anthea later said she would never go through the process again. To this day, she has not been given a copy. Anthea was never shown a transcript or asked to check it. Needless to say, it was never signed. All that didn't matter. It would never see the inside of a court.

As 2011 calendars were discarded and replaced by 2012, I began wondering if anything would ever happen. In March, I got a call from Detective Kristi Faber who was based at Charlestown. Kristi and her former husband had worked with me at Maitland during the late 1990s, but we hadn't spoken since. In 2008, it was Kristi who took Joanne McCarthy's call that gave rise to the groundless allegation I had leaked information about David O'Hearn. Having taken over the investigation of O'Hearn from Shaun McLeod, Kristi now wanted my help. Was I 'aware of any photographs of Father Jim Fletcher taken about 1980?'

It just so happened I was. O'Hearn was trying to deflect blame for the abuse of a child by arguing mistaken identity. I suppose with so many paedophile priests operating in the same Diocese, O'Hearn thought this tactic was worth a try. Kristi needed images of Fletcher to dispel the suggestion. She also asked me about Edmond Gleeson House in Maitland. I remembered Shaun saying that O'Hearn and Fletcher were in a seminary at Edmond Gleeson House where Father Donovan abused girls from the adjoining school. With Shaun no longer on the investigation, Kristi now needed me to fill the gaps. So many people knew little parts, but no one was putting the big picture together. I had been directed not to conduct any Church inquiry, so I explained to Kristi I wasn't allowed to help until I had approval.

Amid Newcastle's staffing crisis, Max Mitchell was promoted to assistant commissioner. His vacancy was filled by Superintendent John Gralton.

John would have received a full briefing on the Church investigation from Max. I emailed John for permission to make inquiries on Kristi's behalf. I outlined the directions given to me by Max to 'cease any involvement in Church paedophilia investigations or dealing with victims', and I posed three questions.

'Was I allowed to conduct inquiries for Detective Faber? Were the directions from Superintendent Mitchell still in force, and if so, for what period? Am I yet able to be told the reasons for those directions?'

It seemed silly to me then, as it does now, that I had to ask permission to do my job. It took John a week to reply. I had to contact Graham Parker. 'He is in a position to guide you in relation to who is best to respond.'

It was a curious response. If anyone else was better placed to assist Kristi, why didn't she ring them? As to my other questions, John said the directions remained in force and I couldn't be told the reasons because it was highly protected.

I told Graham I could assist Kristi 'unless your staff are in a better position to assist her'.

He conceded, 'You know a lot more about this than us. Do whatever you have to.'

I took the opportunity to ask about the Church investigation. It was nearly finished, Graham told me, adding they would be hard pressed to charge anyone on the evidence. I nearly jumped down the phone. There was enough in Denise's and Barbara's statements. I made it clear I would be asking questions if charges didn't eventuate. I didn't apologise for my manner as Graham went quiet.

My comment must have caused Graham some consternation for him to call back. He wanted to know what I believed constituted an offence, as supposedly none of the victims had wanted their abuse reported to police. I couldn't believe it. I knew what was in the statements, I had typed them, so I didn't bother hiding my annoyance.

'Have a bloody read of Denise Laverie's statement!' I told Graham. 'Have a read of my report. I spelled it all out.'

Graham queried, 'What report?'

'You're kidding. The one I sent to Region just before I had to hand over the investigation.'

He insisted he knew nothing of my report and said he had never seen it.

I was vehement in my response. I detailed how I had put it through the TRIM system so it had a number that could be traced. I explained how it had been discussed at the Waratah meeting. And I said that the whole thing stunk. I had even sent an electronic copy to Tony Townsend at Region, so I could prove they got it. They knew about my report.

Graham told me not to get mad at him. It was the first he'd heard of any report and asked if I still had a copy.

'Of course I have. I keep everything. I will send another copy down to you and Jeff. I will even highlight the part about Denise so you can't miss it.'

I couldn't understand how he could say no victim wanted their abuse reported when Denise's statement clearly said, 'I would have been happy for them [the Church hierarchy] to inform the police as long as Anthea and I could remain anonymous so far as Mum was concerned.'

Denise was a principal witness, yet Graham apparently hadn't spoken to her. Barbara's statement mentioned Denis McAlinden admitting to abusing his nieces. Graham must have read Denise's statement where she emphatically said, that if she had known of her uncle's admission, she would have insisted police be involved. On that alone, how could anyone conclude there was insufficient grounds to proceed? If this was Lantle's competency, the investigation was destined to fail.

My report was documented in the minutes of the December meeting, so it couldn't have disappeared. I know that Graham had those minutes, because he later attached them to his affidavit for the Cunneen Inquiry. Didn't he read them? In any case, I still had a copy of my report. I didn't want any more documents going astray, so I emailed the report to Graham and Jeff with a flag to notify me when they opened it. My original report apparently turned up months later. Where it was found, I wasn't told.

I provided Kristi Faber with the photographs she wanted, mostly from Pat Feenan. They depicted Fletcher and Daniel before the abuse started. This rekindled my frustration with Lantle's lack of commitment to investigating Philip Wilson's alleged involvement with Fletcher. I emailed Graham and Jeff urging them to look at Fletcher and others. I pointed out it was possible to track down more than ten victims of Denis McAlinden. Like a school student, Jeff dissected my email into a plethora of questions. He wanted to know everything from why I believed Towards Healing was questionable, to how I knew that survivors not reported to police had been compensated by the Church. I didn't know then that Jeff had declined to complete Helen Keevers' statement, the circumstance of which I will explain shortly. Helen could have answered Jeff's questions if Lantle had been better managed. When I mentioned that Fletcher's and McAlinden's briefs were filed at Maitland together with documents I had seized from the Diocese, Jeff asked, 'Do you mean Maitland Police Station or somewhere else?'

I nearly slapped my forehead. Jeff hadn't chased up the files Shaun intended to collect. Exasperated, I told him, 'I could type for hours on this but clearly you need to sit down with me so I can go through this with you'.

As with Graham, I now told Jeff to read Denise's statement. Jeff should have done so when he completed it, or was there something else they weren't telling me? In my email back to Jeff I told him, 'Jeff, I gather from the comments here you have been told to confine the investigation only to the matters in the statements I supplied. Clearly this needs a task force commitment to look at all matters properly, but for some reason beyond my comprehension the department is reluctant. Over the past fifteen years priest after priest has been charged in the Hunter and Blind Freddy can see the problem goes much deeper. Every time they are investigated it is done piecemeal by different commands ... the same names are cropping up continually with priests charged and those supporting them ... Does our hierarchy just put that down to coincidence?'

In April, Graham and Jeff agreed to sit and discuss the case with me. Two days later, driving back from Sydney, they rang me using hands-free for a professional and comprehensive debriefing. Graham later reported to Carlene York: 'What is, however, quite apparent is the strike force's willingness to accept assistance from Detective Chief Inspector Fox, even when he appeared to display an absence of enthusiasm to do so.'

Come July, police triumphantly announced that Lantle had completed its investigation: 'The investigation has been both arduous and complex in nature and members of the strike force have proven to have been tenacious, thorough and dedicated to the task.'

In September 2012, just before I spoke at the Shine the Light forum at Newcastle Panther's Club, I spoke to Helen Keevers, who told me her statement was never completed. In the minutes of the December 2010 meeting, after I left, Kirren Steel had also raised the significance of Helen's evidence saying she had a 'high level of knowledge about McAlinden's offending'. And of 'other priests and victims'. Helen had also seen 'numerous critical documents outlining such conduct'. One was the document which showed McAlinden admitting to Monsignor Cotter to touching 'the little ones'.

Helen also knew about Anthea and Denise meeting with the Church, and with Bishop Malone's consent, provided them with their documents. Kirren indicated at the meeting that Helen had information about Father Allan Hart and other senior clergy being 'involved in cover-ups'.

She knew about the Encompass Program, saying, 'Archbishop Pell had closed the program down without notice. She indicated that the files relating to the program had been moved by a person, known to her, for storage.'

Kirren relayed Helen urging police to act because they 'would only get one chance at a search warrant because she was certain that Church members would destroy documents'.

Helen's knowledge was disturbing. After the meeting, Max Mitchell and Tony Townsend deliberated before deciding that Graham should contact Paul Jacob to 'assist with Helen'.

These weren't just scurrilous allegations; Helen knew where the bodies were buried, she had seen the evidence.

Despite all this, nearly two years on, Helen's statement wasn't finished. I told her to contact Lantle before the brief was sent to the DPP. Helen looked at me and said, 'I've already done that, but they weren't interested.'

Helen told me Jeff Little explained that it had been decided her statement wasn't needed. They had specific parameters and because her information fell outside those parameters, it wasn't relevant to the task they had at hand. This was the same task force being praised as 'tenacious, thorough and dedicated'. If I had been in their place I would have pushed strenuously for wider parameters.

Helen reminded Jeff that Kirren had promised to give her a copy of the statement they had started. Jeff refused. A copy would not be provided, because the investigation was highly protected. Helen queried why, if her evidence wasn't relevant, it was considered highly protected? Jeff didn't say. Like Anthea's interview, Helen's statement was never signed. Seven years later in 2017, Helen told me she still hadn't seen it.

I was further dismayed when Jeff took fresh statements from Barbara, McAlinden's survivor who was so particular when I took her statement in 2010, and from Mike Stanwell, the former Merriwa school principal. When I took Barbara's statement it was twenty-six pages long and took twenty-eight hours to complete. It was one of the most thorough I had ever typed. She had taken it home to amend it to ensure it was accurate. Mike's statement was just as comprehensive. This time around Jeff again used ERISP, leaving me shaking my head. I had now lost all confidence in Lantle.

CHAPTER 20

THE BOYS' CLUB

Nothing occurs in isolation. This meant that back in early 2010, between pushing for a Church investigation and obtaining statements from Denise, Anthea and others, I was still busy with other things. As Joanne McCarthy wrote about clergy abuse, and Shaun was told to stop looking into the Church concealment offences, I had my hands full with yet another internal investigation.

Since 2009, Raymond Terrace police had been called to numerous domestic disputes involving one of their own. An officer and his ex-wife repeatedly clashed over child custody issues. Both had new partners who were also involved. It was a real shit fight, with allegation and counter-allegation. I was glad not to be involved

In February 2010, police again took no action against this officer when he allegedly made threats to his ex-wife's new partner. Complaining of bias, the boyfriend went to the local court, which issued a Personal Violence Order (PVO). The boyfriend also wrote to the ombudsman and police commissioner. This is when I got involved. Along with another officer, we were told to serve the PVO and seize any firearms the officer had. We weren't happy at being called in to clean this case up so late in the process. The accused was a popular officer and I got along with him. But this day he was aggressive and irrational. He wasn't happy we were at his home. Walking to the back shed, he started taking his guns from a cabinet inside the shed, and swung a barrel past me and slammed other rifles onto a bench. I reported what happened but unsure if his action was intended or not, I gave the officer the benefit of the doubt.

Over time and the odd cup of coffee, the officer reverted to his old self. I even shouted him a round of golf and provided advice over a few beers. The boyfriend then offered an olive branch. He would withdraw the PVO on condition that all future contact be through a third party. The officer agreed, and the boyfriend kept his word.

A few evenings later he reneged on the agreement, phoning the boyfriend again and allegedly threatening, 'Don't go to sleep tonight, I'm gonna come around and kill you, you cunt.'

With the phone on speaker, part of the conversation was purportedly heard by others. Triple-zero was called, with Sergeant Ian Allwood immediately applying for a PVO. He then called the officer, who allegedly told him, 'Don't you come to my fuckin' place and I won't come to the fuckin' station.'

Ian directed police to guard the boyfriend's home and to don ballistics vests, before calling me.

I was asked to ring the officer to calm him down. Unfortunately, the affable colleague I knew had been replaced by an angry ex-husband.

'Don't come around here tonight to serve an AVO on me or that's going to be the least of your worries.'

We were again asked to seize the officer's guns. In the circumstances we should have refused. It turned out the officer had fled and wasn't located until the next day. More worrying incidents followed, on which I won't elaborate. Management remained reluctant to implement any real action.

The whole saga divided the station between the officer's supporters and those believing something needed to be done. The latter didn't have the Commander's support, so remained mute.

I told my Commander of a case I had minor involvement in when Senior Constable Darryl Somerville shot his wife dead at Singleton. 'It happens. Good blokes can lose it.'

I was worried about what could happen, but I was told I didn't look well, which didn't surprise me. My doctor referred me to a psychologist, who instructed me to take time off and distance myself from the case.

As the initial officer in charge, I was never spoken to about anything that had happened and then I wasn't informed of the court hearing to address the PVO.

When I showed the crown solicitor the notes containing the officer's comment to me, which were effectively a threat, they were concerned.

The crown solicitor met with senior police behind closed doors as I typed another report, this time on the police failure to brief the crown solicitor, for which I was later investigated for disclosing unauthorised information.

My evidence in December 2010, for the most part, went unchallenged, but the ostracism began.

While off duty with a broken leg in April 2011, I was again asked to attend court. The officer's supporters were displeased.

There was no criminal charge, just a PVO. With no further incidents and not convinced about the officer's exact threat, the PVO was allowed to expire in May 2011.

While police slapped the officer on the back, the crown solicitor thanked me for my honesty. Even so, I knew what was coming.

The anonymous complaints soon started. Most were trivial, such as files not completed on time. None were upheld, but that wasn't their point. Their volume and relentless nature were intended to wear me down.

When I walked into the meal room some police would turn away while others would leave half-eaten lunches. It was childish stuff. Most police remained sociable, but preferred to do so away from the boys' club.

In June 2011, whilst simultaneously trying to keep an eye on events unfolding with the Church investigation, I received an anonymous letter. Cowards don't like to identify themselves. The departmental letter arrived through internal mail, police emblem and all. Threatening and intimidating, its point being that police 'are appalled at your disgraceful behaviour in trying to sink fellow officers ... after your broken leg, we all feel a great regret it wasn't your neck'.

This was the boys' club or the Brotherhood identified by Justice Wood. Not only was it alive, it was flourishing.

Initially the letter stayed under the radar. Instead of recording it as a crime or initiating a complaint, a senior officer filed it as a local management issue.

When I refused to be intimidated, the Brotherhood upped the ante by targeting my family. Police corruption has no scruples. The next letter, departmental envelope and all, was mailed to Penny at our home. It repeated the threats and intimidation. Penny had a breakdown. Our doctor placed her on medication and referred her for counselling. The police force offered to pay, but Penny refused, believing that senior police were just as culpable as the letter's author.

I was interviewed by so many police over so many complaints I lost track. Issues were broken into separate investigations so no one investigator ever understood the whole picture. When I returned from leave, the ostracism and anonymous complaints resumed with zeal.

Another senior officer was the next to interview me. Penny had driven me to work in our private car the night of the alleged threats when police had to guard the boyfriend's name. When I told this officer she overheard my request for charges to be laid, he didn't seem happy. He determined I receive a warning notice for allowing Penny to overhear the conversation. Penny had heard hundreds of police conversations, particularly when I was called out in the middle of the night. It was like my treatment after the pepper-spray investigation all over again. Knowing more was coming, I took leave.

CHAPTER 21

ANOTHER GOOD PRIEST

Stories coming out of Ballarat sounded remarkably like those in the Hunter. Paedophile clergy protected, priests moved from parish to parish while bishops guarded the Church's good name. Detective Sergeant Kevin Carson had investigated his fair share of clergy abuse in the Eureka City. In 2011, Kevin submitted a report suggesting up to forty clergy abuse victims may have committed suicide. It was largely ignored by police, but all hell broke loose in April 2012 when the media became aware. The next week, as I implored Graham Parker to expand his investigation in the Hunter, the state of Victoria did just that with Premier Ted Baillieu announcing a Parliamentary Inquiry into clergy child sexual abuse. Not a Royal Commission, but a step closer.

The first attempt to discredit Kevin Carson happened when a report by Victoria Police fell into the hands of the Catholic Church and media saying Kevin's figures couldn't be substantiated. Operation Plangere, set up to address Kevin's claims, found only one suicide connected to clergy abuse. With the swiftness of Swiss Guards some media commentators attacked Kevin, inferring the Parliamentary Inquiry was instigated by fraud.

Trouble was, Plangere and those commentators hadn't done their homework.

Louise Milligan wasn't a commentator, but an investigative journalist who knew all about homework. Interviewing friends and family of suicide victims, she discovered that police hadn't spoken to them. Not one. Those families now told Louise a completely different story. When abuse survivors gave evidence to the Child Abuse Royal Commission, one survivor, Philip Nagle, showed a Ballarat class photo pointing out one third of his class had committed suicide. Police never spoke to Philip. Nor did police speak to Kevin Carson, who could have pointed them in the right direction. Ballarat abuse survivor Peter Blenkiron later told me he provided one detective with more names not on Kevin's list, only to be told, 'We don't want to open a can of worms.'

Dr Judy Curtin, a lawyer who earned her doctorate by examining clergy child sexual abuse, raised forty-five suicides around Ballarat related to clergy abuse before saying, 'Police supposedly investigated these forty-five suicides, but I got hold of the police report, and it was rubbish. They didn't investigate all of them, and they found only one was related to sexual abuse. That's a joke, and it's so terribly insulting ... But sadly in Ballarat the way child sexual abuse was historically investigated is a reflection of so many cities and regional towns across the whole bloody world.'

As pro-church commentators retreated, the Plangere report was exposed as ineptly compiled and misleading. Kevin had to endure the slings and arrows until vindicated when the truth eventually emerged.

•

Like Denis McAlinden, Finian Egan was a Catholic priest who arrived in Australia from Ireland. Within two years he was sexually abusing children and being moved from one Sydney parish to another.

Broken Rites was first contacted about Egan in 2003. Over the next five years, a second survivor made contact, then a third and fourth until the number reached six. Despite being from various parishes and not knowing one another, all had remarkably similar stories. In 2008 one of Egan's survivors complained to the Catholic Church. Instead of informing police, the Church began its own investigation. Soon after, Egan returned to Ireland, where, in spite of being suspended, he continued performing mass.

The Church investigation was still going two years later when one of Egan's survivors bypassed Towards Healing and went directly to police. Broken Rites spoke to Egan's other survivors, with a number agreeing to give evidence.

Politician Greg Smith was a former president of the Right to Life Association and St Thomas More Society. Smith's website proclaimed him as 'a man of enduring faith and commitment ... heavily involved in the life of the Catholic Church'. During his inaugural 2007 speech to NSW Parliament, before any of the complaints against Egan were made public, Smith even expounded the virtues of Father Finian Egan.

When Barry O'Farrell won the 2011 election, Greg Smith became the state's Attorney-General. Smith appointed Damien Tudehope as his chief of staff.

By April 2012, Egan had returned to Australia from Ireland and was charged with sexual offences against two girls aged eleven and sixteen and a fourteen-year-old boy. Barrister Anthony Tudehope, brother of the Attorney-General's chief of staff, represented Egan. When one of

Egan's survivors contacted the *Sydney Morning Herald*, Greg Smith found himself in hot water. The woman alleged Smith downplayed her allegation by saying it was merely an attempt to get money from the Church. Smith denied the comment. Smith told reporters he continued to pray for Father Egan. No mention was made of praying for Egan's alleged victims.

When the NSW opposition later tried to obtain Greg Smith's briefing notes concerning Egan, Damien Tudehope denied them access. A conflict of interest was raised by their political opponents, but Premier O'Farrell refused to intervene.

Egan was gaoled in December 2013 for child rape and multiple indecent assaults. Many considered his minimum four-year sentence lenient. He was paroled in December 2017.

•

The same month Damien Tudehope refused to produce the Attorney-General's notes, a tip-off from Broken Rites led ABC-TV's *Four Corners* to screen 'Unholy Silence'. It started with survivor anger directed at Towards Healing and the Melbourne Response, before spotlighting the crimes of Father John Farrell, referred to in the program as 'Father F' due to a court suppression order. What pricked my attention was the mention of Father Brian Lucas, the Church's Mr Fix It.

In 1983, parents on the rich black plains of Moree told Monsignor Frank Ryan his fellow priest, John Farrell, was sexually abusing altar boys. One boy's father had gone to police, however no action was taken. The following year Armidale's Bishop Henry Kennedy was made aware of Farrell's offending by parents of abused children. He too did nothing, beyond moving the priest.

In 1987, fifteen-year-old Damian Jurd and his father went to police. The Church already knew Farrell had abused other boys, but the Church had managed to silence them. The Church said nothing to police or the court. Instead the Church hired barrister Chester Porter QC to savage the boy in the witness box. The magistrate, an acquaintance of Farrell, took the priest's word above that of Damian. Dismissing the charges, the magistrate made a suppression order prohibiting any reporting on the case. Damian was devastated, with his life descending into depression and drugs.

Nevertheless, word about Farrell spread faster than a Pilliga scrub fire. The Church realised he had to be moved. Farrell was sent to work with Father Finian Egan at Carlingford, before again moving him, this time to the Parramatta Diocese, where twelve-year-old Daniel Powell and others were targeted.

A decade on, consumed by drugs, alcohol and depression, it was alleged Daniel ineptly demanded compensation from his abuser. Daniel claimed Farrell paid him a sum of money, which he unwisely accepted, on the understanding he not complain to police. Whatever the truth, Farrell spoke to a police officer, who he described as 'a good mate', resulting in Daniel being charged with extortion. Daniel had not gone to police with his abuse allegations before being arrested.

In the lead-up to Daniel's 2004 trial, his lawyers did some digging. They discovered a 1992 letter of a meeting between Farrell and three senior clergy. Daniel's lawyers kept their powder dry until Farrell gave evidence, then confronted him on the witness stand: 'I suggest to you that at the meeting you made certain admissions to those priests that you had oral sex with young boys.'

Under oath, Farrell admitted it was true. Deafening silence. The jury found Daniel not guilty. Despite the letter and

Farrell's admission, NSW Police and the DPP did not pursue charges against Farrell for those crimes. The crucial letter was then forgotten as it was filed in court archives, and would not surface for another eight years.

In 1992 Farrell had been summoned to a meeting with three senior clergy at Sydney's St Mary's Cathedral. Under NSW law, any admissions should have been reported to police. Farrell had been stood down from ministry, but would not be laicised until 2005. Even so, police were told nothing.

In 2012, ABC-TV's *Four Corners* obtained the damning letter. Written by Father Wayne Peters to Bishop Manning after the 1992 meeting, it recorded Farrell admitting, 'there had been five boys around the age of ten and eleven that he [Farrell] had sexually interfered with in varying degrees in the years approximately 1982 to 1984 while he was the assistant priest at Moree'.

The abuse occurred mostly in the priest's car during altar boy trips from Moree to Narrabri. Farrell's admissions to his fellow priests were disturbing: 'Over a period of approximately twelve months he fondled the genitals of each of these boys and, to quote, "sucked off their dicks". This was done on about a monthly basis over a period of twelve months.'

Peters never named the altar boys – Church records, however, could be tracked down. The letter said little about the boys' welfare, but did express concern for Mother Church: 'The possibility always remains that one or some of the boys involved may bring criminal charges against Father F, with subsequent grave harm to the priesthood and the Church.'

As the scandal erupted following the *Four Corners* story, Cardinal Pell gave a media conference to defend his priests, however, was left out on a limb when he used a file note made by a senior clergyman to say Farrell made no admissions: 'I would take the word of the three priests against that allegation.'

Pell's position became difficult to maintain when it was revealed the file note was only written in 2012, weeks before the story went to air, whereas Peters' letter was written eight days after the 1992 meeting.

When the full content of Peters' letter became public, the Church changed tack with Brian Lucas telling the ABC's *AM* program that Farrell admitted abusing boys, but was 'cautious not to incriminate himself,' specifically by not naming his victims – and without names, they couldn't go to police.

Over a two-year period in a town the size of Moree, it wouldn't be difficult to discover the boys' names. With Farrell having admitted his crimes, how did Lucas know Farrell wouldn't divulge more to police, including the names?

By not telling police, Lucas insisted he had done nothing wrong. Sydney University senior law lecturer Miiko Kumar thought otherwise: 'Now the section (316) doesn't require that specific information be given as to names. I mean, that's a matter for the police to go and investigate.'

Barrister Andrew Morrison SC of the Australian Lawyers Alliance believed the case should have been pursued: 'The only excuse that was given was that they didn't know the names of the altar boys. Well, of course they didn't, they didn't ask.'

As for Peters, he was laying low. Years later, Peters would tell the Child Abuse Royal Commission he stood by the content of his 1992 letter.

With so many contradictions and counterclaims, calls grew for the NSW Government to act and for police to investigate. There were even rumblings for a Child Abuse Royal Commission. Former DPP Director Nicholas Cowdery weighed in, telling the *Sydney Morning Herald* there were grounds to proceed against senior clergy: 'I can't, frankly, see any reason why it would not proceed.'

The government remained silent, no doubt hoping the storm would blow over. It didn't.

A week after the *Four Corners* story aired, Patrick Parkinson, the law professor hired by the Church to review Towards Healing, called for a Royal Commission. The government still didn't respond. Instead, NSW Police announced Strike Force Glenroe. Many were sceptical, including Damien Jurd's mother, who said that after her son 'went to the police' years before, he told her, 'They treated me really badly.'

Another cynical parent said, 'Look, you might notice an edge in my voice. That's simply because it's twenty-nine years too late and there's a lot of victims since.'

When the allegations against Farrell first surfaced in 1984 and 1986, the Church did nothing. In 1987, the Church financed Farrell's defence and was later obligated to pay substantial compensation to his victims. But money wasn't the answer. All Daniel Powell and Damien Jurd wanted was justice, the very thing the Church denied them. In the depths of depression, Damien took his own life in 2001. Daniel hanged himself in 2007. Both were dead before their twenty-eighth birthdays. The Church knew the truth. It could have saved them, instead it chose to defend Farrell and attack his victims. Now it offered a hollow apology and a Church-sponsored inquiry.

The Church inquiry meant NSW Police and the Church would now be running simultaneous investigations. How could one not interfere with the other? To me it was simple: concealing a serious crime was a criminal offence, and investigating criminal offences was the role of police. It was all well and good for an institution to examine rule breaches, but they had no business when it came to state laws. Bernard

Barrett from Broken Rites pointed out the obvious: 'They should leave this sort of thing to the police or preferably a royal commission to investigate the systematic covering up or concealing or ignoring of these crimes.'

The Church wasn't told to back off. Instead Premier O'Farrell asked the Church to provide police with the results of its independent inquiry. When police declined to confirm if Glenroe would investigate the alleged cover-up, I suspected a lot was happening behind the scenes.

The Catholic Church's Independent Inquiry was unable to decide whose memory was accurate and whose was inaccurate. It resulted in no recommendations to refer any person to police.

Farrell wasn't interviewed. Under oath in the Supreme Court, Farrell had admitted the content of Peters' letter was true. Surely the man at the centre had to be interviewed. Police should have interviewed Farrell and executed search warrants for any other potentially damning documents. It was basic investigating.

Academics and lawyers, including Andrew Morrison SC, were dismayed: 'The failure [of the inquiry] to grapple seriously with the conduct' of the clergy 'inspires no confidence in the conclusions in the report.'

He was right. Where were the police? The Church had effectively investigated itself. The Parramatta Diocese triumphantly announced, 'As soon as the Bishops received [the Church]'s report, a full copy was given to the NSW police.'

It was all very predictable, with Premier O'Farrell praising the report and NSW Police closing the case.

'No criminal action is being taken by police based on the information in the report.'

•

In March 2013 I met a controversial former priest, Kevin Lee. Kevin married in secret to make a point: marriage wasn't an impediment to being a priest. The Catholic Church wasn't happy. Unlike priests sexually abusing kids, Kevin was expeditiously thrown out of the priesthood.

Working at Hoxton Park close to where I grew up, Kevin managed to contact me and ask if we could meet, saying he had something important to discuss, which couldn't be said over the phone.

A half-hour coffee turned into a full day. Kevin spoke about his wife, Josefina, and their plans to settle in the Philippines, before revealing the real purpose of why he wanted to meet with me.

I would like to say more about that day, and the documents Kevin showed me, but for legal reasons I am unable to reveal what Kevin disclosed, beyond saying that as a witness in the Independent Church Inquiry, he was deeply troubled by the NSW Police decision not to investigate the alleged concealment of Farrell's crimes.

Kevin and I stayed in contact. Months after our March 2013 meeting Kevin moved to the Philippines. In November, and only weeks after becoming a father, Kevin disappeared in Typhoon Haiyan. Days later police found his body.

CHAPTER 22

FALLING ON DEAF EARS

As the stories of Fathers Farrell and Egan played out, I contacted Pat Feenan about her photographs of Father Fletcher to assist in the trial of Father David O'Hearn. Pat was happy to help, and she took the opportunity to say she had written a book. Well, it wasn't really a book. She had started writing to get everything out of her head and had been playing around with it for years. Pat asked if I would have a look, just to make sure the legal parts were accurate and that sort of thing.

Collecting her folder of loose pages on my way home, I could see Pat was anxious about letting her manuscript go. It held her thoughts, frustrations, anguish and so much more. It spoke about the impact of the abuse, not only on Daniel, but on herself, her marriage, her other children and their extended family. They had all been victims. Like the scar around Daniel's neck, it had faded, but the ordeal remained. Writing helped.

Reading through the manuscript I soon became absorbed. To my mind, apart from minor corrections it was perfect. So, what did Pat plan to do? She still wasn't sure. Maybe self-publish, just for friends and family. I told her it could go further. It could tell others of the real damage caused by clergy abuse. Pat said she would think about it.

Around the same time as I read Pat's manuscript, I spoke to our neighbours. Helena and Paul are really more than neighbours, they're friends. Paul enjoys a beer and a barbecue, and together we love a good laugh around a fire. Like me, Helena is a voracious reader.

'I've just finished a book you have to read, Peter. It brought me to tears.'

I asked what it was called.

'*Hell on the Way to Heaven*. It's written by a lady in Melbourne whose daughters were abused by a priest.'

'The author isn't Chrissie Foster, by chance?'

I had followed Chrissie and Anthony's story in the media and finished reading her book in days. Books can be powerful. Like Pat's manuscript, Chrissie's story had a significant impact on me. With the stories of Farrell and Egan playing in the news, I was convinced more needed to be done. In the lead up to the Newcastle Shine the Light Forum, I also spoke to Helen Keevers. That's when I learned that police had no interest in completing her statement, or pursuing the other issues she had raised with Kirren Steel and me. My anger and frustration were all building as the forum approached. All my experiences were now about to cumulate in a life-changing act.

•

When I see the footage of me on stage that day in September 2012, I cringe. My face full of emotion, contorted, eyes welling and voice trembling. I didn't realise how bad I looked until shown the vision later. However, it accurately reflected how

I felt. Although clergy sexual abuse didn't happen in my family, I had seen the harm.

Walking to the microphone I had no idea what I was going to say, just that I had to say something. There was no plan, just words borne of emotion. I raised what Premier O'Farrell had publicly stated: that the police force 'had it under control' and 'a Royal Commission might prejudice police investigations or prosecutions'.

Both Police Minister Gallacher and Deputy Police Commissioner Kaldas had denied knowledge of such advice, leaving the premier a little red-faced. I told the auditorium I too didn't accept Premier O'Farrell's excuse. I might not have made friends in Macquarie Street with what I said, but the audience applauded their agreement. I spoke about my removal from the Church investigation before saying the only way to address the cover-up of clergy abuse was through a Royal Commission. When I finished the audience was on its feet.

Sitting back down, my head was spinning. I didn't remember everything I said, my mind was still worrying about the consequences. When the meeting finished I tried to leave, but my path was blocked by handshakes and well-wishers. Pat Feenan managed to squeeze through and say she would see me outside. It must have been half an hour before the crowd finally began to dwindle.

At the back of the auditorium a man waited inconspicuously. He was clearly troubled, wanting to catch me alone. I saw the tears before he spoke. Introducing himself, Peter Creigh said, 'I want to apologise.'

Confused, I inquired, 'Apologise? Apologise for what?'

'I'm another victim of Fletcher who didn't have the guts to come forward.'

Peter carried guilt like an anvil, believing if he had come forward others might have been spared. I told him he had nothing to apologise for. It was never easy speaking up. With Fletcher dead, little could now be done. But he had more to tell me, much more. In 1976 at the age of fifteen, Peter reported to another priest, not just once, but twice, that Father Fletcher had abused him. It happened the year Daniel Feenan was born. Peter told me he confided in a priest, who had later become a senior clergyman. If this man had acted, Daniel and others could have been saved. My head was swimming from other events that day, and now I was drowning. I told Peter it was unlikely I would go back to work, that police wouldn't be happy with what I had just done. Nevertheless, I urged him to see them. He agreed.

Peter's information was proof that Strike Force Lantle should have been investigating Fletcher all along. Lantle shouldn't have been so highly protective and secretive, it should have been using the media, calling for survivors and witnesses to come forward to the police. I'm not suggesting police should disclose everything – I have held information back from the media myself – but you need to use the media in proactive policing as opposed to hoping witnesses walk themselves in. Police in Newcastle saw Joanne McCarthy as a troublemaker, nothing more. She had caused resources to be wasted on a case they considered hopeless. She was treated as an enemy, and the investigation suffered.

The fact Peter Creigh attended this forum organised by Joanne and the *Newcastle Herald* was further proof police should have been using the media. As I walked outside, I saw Pat standing with her friends. It wasn't easy looking her in the face after speaking to another survivor who had been sexually abused by the same priest who had raped her son, knowing that if the Church had acted, her son and others could have been spared.

Pat and her friends were all worried, too worried to let me leave. Apparently, I didn't look well, and they would stay with me until I settled down.

Away shopping in Sydney, Penny had no idea what I had done, so I phoned. I didn't want her unnecessarily alarmed by hearing something on the radio. I could be in trouble, big trouble, I told her. Penny later said I didn't actually say why. I was vague and not making a lot of sense. All she wanted to do was get home to me.

Over lunch I told Pat about Peter Creigh. Still distressed, I forgot his surname, although I did remember what we had discussed. Pat was just as shocked as I was at learning another survivor of Fletcher's sexual abuse had told a second priest, and nothing was done to save her Daniel. Eventually I pulled myself together and went home. Pat called that night, still worried about me, and introduced herself to Penny.

After the meeting, the *Newcastle Herald* received a host of online comments calling for a Royal Commission and asking why Premier O'Farrell was so opposed. Pressure was building, but the problem was the abuse being discussed and calls for a Royal Commission was mostly confined to the Hunter Valley. Like the *Illawarra Mercury* two decades earlier, the *Newcastle Herald* had raised awareness, but it was a regional publication and struggled to reach the bigger state and national audiences. Those in the Hunter are used to being ignored by politicians in Sydney, and that's exactly what happened.

Surprisingly, I didn't get any calls from police, but I knew they would be talking. After everything I had been through I was under no illusions about what would happen if I went back. I came to the realisation I would probably never return and remained on extended leave.

•

When Pat published *Holy Hell,* I wrote the foreword. David Shoebridge kindly organised Parliament House for her upcoming book launch in December 2012.

Before that, Penny and I had already booked a trip to Tasmania for late October. Before we left, Joanne McCarthy phoned. The Newcastle forum had been a real success, but her campaign for a Child Abuse Royal Commission was losing momentum, she told me. A senior police officer lending support had been helpful, but now Joanne wanted me to do more. I wasn't so sure. I had stuck my head out a fair way and was lucky thus far not to have it cut off. It effectively ended my career. Wasn't that enough? I was still worried about departmental charges. It was different for Joanne: clergy child sexual abuse and its cover-up was undoubtedly a tough story, and Joanne had endured criticism and suggestions she was obsessed and running a vendetta against the Church. But it was her job. Unlike me, it didn't threaten her career. Quite the opposite. Her articles earned praise, awards and recognition. Of course, this wasn't the reason she was doing it. Joanne was a journalist doing what journalists do, albeit going beyond. She deserved all the acclaim that came her way, but as sure as hell the police force wouldn't be looking to pin a medal on me. Mentioning Pat Feenan's scheduled book launch a few months later in December 2012, I told Joanne I would think about saying more then.

'That will be too late.'

Joanne explained that a lot of momentum had built up, the public was on board and politicians were under pressure.

By December, all that would have died away. Once more giving her the brush-off, I said I would think about it. In reality, I probably had no intention of doing even that.

Penny looked at me. We had been through a lot together. Picking up the gist of my phone conversation with Joanne she agreed. 'You've done enough. Let her find someone else.'

Penny was right. I had put in well over thirty years investigating some terrible crimes. I had suffered, and so had my family. Penny was there every step of the way, the late-night call-outs and me not coming home for days. I had missed our daughter's eighth birthday party when a woman and her kids were found murdered in the Watagan Mountains. Penny understood. I had done more than enough, and the effects of PTSD were showing. Joanne would have to find someone else.

•

When Pat invited us to afternoon tea I felt it was okay. It was impossible to return to the police force. Pat was no longer part of my work and had instead become a friend. It was time Pat and Penny met. When Pat cut the end from a date slice fresh from the oven, Penny didn't hesitate to say, 'Don't throw that away, I like the crispy bit. And would you mind if I have some butter on it?'

Pat laughed. 'I like a person who doesn't hold back.'

It was the beginning of what would become an enduring friendship. We hadn't mentioned our upcoming holiday, so when Pat next called she was surprised to learn we were in Tasmania. 'You're not going to Hobart, by chance?'

'Yes, we're spending the last few days there.'

Daniel, her son, was now working in Hobart and Pat said he would love to hear from me. Failed relationships are a common consequence for abuse survivors; Daniel and Donna separated, but maintained a warm, amicable relationship in raising their son. Pat passed on his number, and I agreed to give him a call. Penny and I planned to be at Salamanca Markets two days before we flew home, so I invited Daniel to join us for morning tea.

We met with a warm handshake and introduction. 'This is my wife, Penny.'

Penny knew Daniel's story. Not all of it, but enough. The subject wasn't broached that day; it didn't need to be. Morning coffee turned to lunch, and then afternoon drinks. We spoke about Daniel's job and his hopes for the future. Conversation was easy. Between Hobart's four seasons of sunshine and showers, Penny left Daniel and me together as she squeezed in some shopping. It was a pleasant afternoon.

Penny was impressed. She thought Daniel articulate, charming and easy on the eye. I smiled. 'Perhaps I shouldn't have introduced you?'

Over the next few days Penny was quiet. I had no idea what she was thinking when out of the blue she said, 'I think you should do it.'

I looked at her quizzically. 'Do what?'

'Whatever it is Joanne wants you to do.'

Having met Pat and Daniel, Penny saw they were people just like us. A family like ours. The only difference was they had been through hell, and we had been spared. What happened to Daniel could so easily have happened to one of our own. We were lucky, that was all.

It was a big call. I explained to Penny we wouldn't just be taking on the Catholic Church, but the police force and politicians all at the same time. I speculated on the consequences and the chances of us coming out unscathed. They weren't good. I wanted Penny to know what we were letting ourselves in for. I won't say we weren't scared – we were shit-scared – but whatever happened, we would face it together.

On the flight home I toyed with ideas of my own, wondering what Joanne had in mind. While speaking at public forums was all well and good, I knew we were preaching to the converted. The public weren't fools, they knew something was seriously wrong. That's why politicians were uncomfortable, but many didn't want to risk alienating the Catholic vote. I thought about that. I didn't want to come across as anti-Catholic. I wasn't. All the survivors I had dealt with were Catholic, plus I had a long line of Catholics in my own family. Maybe I could use that? Penny and I understood it could have been us. I wanted politicians to consider the same.

When I called Joanne, she didn't know what to say. She was grateful I was prepared to come on board, but unsure what we could do. The whole campaign had been exhausting for her and, for now, she had run out of ideas. When I suggested writing an open letter to the premier she jumped at it. Asking what I should write, Joanne returned serve: it had to be my own work.

I spent a few days playing around with the words. I praised police for arresting clergy, but there seemed no end to it. The Church apologising and compensating wasn't enough. Someone needed to go after the system, those who harboured paedophile priests and covered up their crimes. If the protection network was dismantled (and how else can I describe it when I was aware offending priests were moved again and again), I reasoned, the Church's child abusers would have nowhere to hide. Like the drug trade – you can lock up all the users you like, but unless you target further up the food chain, nothing will change. Police needed to go after senior clergy who hid the abusers and concealed their crimes.

The line I wrote that most journalists seized upon was: 'I can testify from my own experience that the Church covers up, silences victims, hinders police investigations, alerts offenders, destroys evidence and moves priests to protect the good name of the Church.' I had seen evidence of it all.

At the time I was still a Christian, so I finished by saying the Church didn't want a Royal Commission but 'God knows we need one'.

I sent the original to Premier Barry O'Farrell before emailing another to his office. Joanne wanted a copy for the paper; after all, it was an open letter. I insisted nothing go out until the following day. I wanted to give the premier time to reply. With no response, Joanne ran my letter. Nothing. I learned through Joanne and other reporters that the premier would not be responding to my plea. Various people told me all I had apparently achieved was to piss him off.

CHAPTER 23

TWENTY-ONE MINUTES

Suzie Smith's role in the lead-up to the Child Abuse Royal Commission went largely unnoticed. A Sydney based award-winning journalist with the ABC-TV, Suzie shied away from the limelight. Occasionally she appeared in front of the cameras, but her real strength was behind them. Over the years she had worked on many stories of abuse within the Catholic Church, picking up on the disproportionately high number of cases within the Maitland–Newcastle Diocese. We spoke on a number of occasions well before Joanne and I started talking. In May 2008, Suzie wrote a story on Anthony and Chrissie Foster's pursuit of a papal apology for World Youth Day. After speaking to Daniel and Pat Feenan in the lead up to that event, Suzie felt my voice might add some weight. Meeting at Newcastle Police Station, I told her I supported a papal apology, and we discussed clergy abuse in the Hunter.

Calls for an apology were detracting from the papal visit. In his role as World Youth Day organiser, Bishop Anthony Fisher must have become annoyed as he then fired back his now infamous comment about 'people dwelling crankily on old wounds'.

Coming only months after the Fosters' eldest daughter committed suicide, and with other abuse survivors still living with nightmares, he was rightly condemned. Old wounds indeed. The papal apology happened, thanks in part to Suzie's journalism.

Like Joanne, Suzie saw the bigger picture. It wasn't all about individual priests. The underlying issue was the systemic cover-up.

Suzie and I had spoken a few times since her papal apology story four years earlier. She was now following events in Newcastle and the Hunter Valley closely.

With Premier O'Farrell ignoring my letter, Joanne and I were out of options. Suzie now leapt to our rescue. I needed a bigger audience, she told me. Was I prepared to go on national television?

'When?'

'Tonight!'

Suzie did the organising while Penny and I hurriedly packed a few things and started on the three-hour drive to Sydney. All the way down I tried to think of what to say. I wanted to win Premier O'Farrell over. So far all I had done was gain his indignation. Was it the cost of a Royal Commission? Surely the protection of children came before money? I had read somewhere that Premier O'Farrell was Catholic with two sons, and I wondered if I could use that angle.

After dropping everything at our hotel, we met Suzie and walked to the ABC-TV's Sydney studios in Ultimo. The landscape had changed since I'd worked this part of the city during the 1970s. This was where my policing career started, and now it would be where it finished.

I remember being impressed by the size of the ABC-TV foyer. We had a whirlwind tour as Penny and I were introduced to producers, camera operators and others. I think Suzie realised, more than I did at the time, the significance of what was about to happen. The interview would take place a few hours before it went to air. We had time for a quick bite, then it was downstairs to the studio. While I had been impressed with everything above ground, below it was more like a bunker, something to do with the sound. Suzie pointed out the make-up room to our right. Being a bloke's bloke, I turned up my nose. 'I don't need to do that, do I?'

Apparently so; they needed to make sure my face wasn't too shiny for the camera.

Tony Jones, who would conduct the interview, sat in another chair. We exchanged a few pleasantries, but that was it. I expected some questions about what I would say, but nothing. Police lawyers would later ask for our script. There was none. Maybe they felt the interview went too well not to have been orchestrated.

What surprised me was how calm I was, even tranquil. It was the complete opposite to the Newcastle forum. This time Penny was present and I was prepared. While I was calm, I couldn't say the same for Penny. She understood how big this was. While supporting everything I was doing, she was understandably nervous.

Suzie asked Penny if she would like to watch from upstairs. No, she wanted to stay with me, so Suzie organised a chair in the studio. I was shown to a seat, and that was it. I had no idea what I would be asked. Tony would fire questions from Suzie's research. That's how it worked. I was now in their hands.

Although Tony called me 'detective chief inspector', I realised that was now in the past. Reading from my letter to the premier, he asked what I thought was the worst of it (child abuse). The Church was well versed at playing down images; they knew the harm it caused. Pro-church commentators regurgitated the same soft language followed by never-ending apologies. If there were to be a Child Abuse Royal Commission I knew I had to shock, to shake people into awareness. In her book *Holy Hell*, Pat Feenan raised one of Daniel's rapes, the one in Paterson Park. It was an image seared into my mind too, so that was the rape I recounted. It said so much about what happened, and continued happening, to many. It possibly upset people. If that's what it took to awaken the public consciousness, then so be it. It was the truth, the terrible truth. Not many allowed their story to be told. I am indebted to Daniel Feenan for finding the courage to allow his to be shared. The Australian nation is even more indebted, given what it achieved.

Tony cited figures he described as shocking, even astonishing. Four hundred victims, fourteen clergy charged, six Catholic teachers convicted and three more priests currently on trial, and that was just in the Hunter Valley. He didn't mention the twelve other priests involved in civil claims for which the Diocese had compensated survivors.

'How does this much evil get concentrated in one small area?'

It was something many were asking. Police had the same figures, but weren't even acknowledging the question.

'I don't think it takes a detective chief inspector to work that out, Tony. Alarm bells were ringing there for me many, many years ago ... it was quite evident that something was going on.'

I expected the entire interview to focus on my letter and calls for a Royal Commission. I didn't know Tony was going to ask about my being removed from the McAlinden case. That was a surprise. Once it was out there, though, I wasn't going to hide what went on. When asked why I had been removed, I told the truth: I didn't know. When he said Assistant Commissioner Carlene York claimed it was because I was attached to another command, I said it was the first time I had heard that. Tony's next queries weren't as much questions as statements: 'You were a logical person to be on the taskforce? ... It's going to seem passing strange to most observers, as it does to me, I must say.'

His words, not mine.

I was careful not to touch on any area that might prejudice a prosecution. I also squeezed in that I wasn't being critical of all police, particularly those doing a great job of arresting paedophile priests. Nevertheless, I was pleased to return to questions about a Child Abuse Royal Commission. It gave me the opportunity to make a personal plea to Premier O'Farrell. Like my own family, I said, his sons weren't abused, but that was pure luck. Others hadn't been so lucky. I tried appealing to his compassion, telling Premier O'Farrell this was a real chance to 'stop more victims from being abused'.

The interview ended as quickly as it began. As the lights came on, Penny walked over and the studio door flew open. Suzie almost ran to join us. When I asked Tony, 'Was it good?'

Suzie answered for him, 'Good? It was fucking brilliant.' She turned to Tony. 'Twenty-one minutes, but we're not cutting any of it, Tony, not a second.'

Tony didn't need convincing. There was talk about speaking to a producer to make sure everything went in. I was a little perplexed.

'Twenty-one minutes, what does that mean?'

Suzie explained. 'No interview goes more than fifteen minutes, not even with the prime minister. Your interview went six minutes over, but we're not cutting any of it. Not a second. It was fantastic.'

I was pleased, but I saw they had a lot to do before it went to air. Penny and I were now in the way, so we said our goodbyes and walked to our hotel.

Sitting in our room we waited for the program to begin. Despite assurances, I remained apprehensive. I had done a lot of media over the years, but nothing like this. Watching the interview, I sat critiquing: I should have said this or mentioned that. Penny pointed out I couldn't have said everything. Despite the program's late time slot, I hoped it would reach enough people.

In the lead-up to all this Joanne had told me we shouldn't knock back any media interviews after the program went to air. We needed all the publicity we could get. This might be our final roll of the dice. If a Child Abuse Royal Commission didn't happen now, it might never. Penny and I put our mobiles on charge and went to bed.

We didn't need an alarm, because the phones rang early. Some journalists were passed on by the ABC-TV or *Newcastle Herald*, others found alternative ways to track us down. I soon realised the interview reached a bigger audience than I imagined. Not only that, it was being replayed on news programs and portions loaned to other networks. It ignited a conversation – a national conversation that needed to happen. Newspaper, television and radio networks began arriving for *grabs*. In the middle of all this, I got a call from a senior officer. We exchanged pleasantries before he directed me to stop talking to the media. I suppose he felt he had to do something. I thanked him for his call and politely explained I wouldn't be complying. My being on sick leave, he then rang my doctor to find out my next medical appointment so he could attend and personally serve me with a departmental direction to cease talking to the media, or for my doctor to pass it on. I don't know who was more outraged, my doctor or me. After making it blatantly clear that wasn't going to happen, she rang me. My email to this officer wasn't as polite as our earlier conversation.

It wasn't long before a journalist asked to speak to me in confidence. Some police were saying I was mentally unstable and anything I said should be treated with caution. That's how it started.

It was the same tactic used against Detective Sergeant Philip Arantz. In the 1970s, Arantz discovered that NSW Police were fudging crime figures. Well, not just fudging – massively understating them. The public were being lied to in order to make police and the government look good. Getting no support from senior officers, Arantz gave the correct figures to the media. It caused an uproar, earning him the ire of both the commissioner and premier. Police then embarked on a vicious campaign to discredit him. The police medical officer certified Arantz mentally ill and admitted him to a psychiatric ward. Days later he was discharged with hospital records recording, 'Possible political expediency in bringing pressure to bear on patient's admission.'

Arantz was suspended before being dishonourably discharged. It took decades for Arantz to be exonerated, by which time the former commissioner and premier had long since passed. Arantz was cleared, with the NSW Government paying out a tidy sum in compensation. I wasn't admitted to a psychiatric ward, but the tactic was comparable. Joanne McCarthy hadn't been spared either, saying, 'There were a lot of people within the church and the police happy to run the line that I was mad, that I was obsessed.'

The morning after my *Lateline* interview, Premier O'Farrell announced a Special Commission of Inquiry to examine my comments about police. Many thought it a knee-jerk reaction. For months the premier had refused to hold a Child Abuse Royal Commission, but when police conduct was questioned, he acted quickly.

Prominent individuals criticised the premier's announcement. Politician David Shoebridge called it a 'half-baked inquiry' and 'a decoy'; '[t]he crime of sexual abuse of children was not limited to the Hunter and it is just extraordinary that the focus of this inquiry will be the police's handling of abuse and not the actions of the Church'.

Unlike a Royal Commission, a Special Commission is adversarial, with rules similar to a trial. The question was, who would be on trial?

Everything happened overnight, literally. Considering the late hour my interview went to air, the premier must have been busy to put an inquiry together and find someone to lead it before his announcement the next day. Margaret Cunneen wasn't a judge, but a DPP barrister. Cunneen rose in the legal profession when women were still fighting career stereotyping and striving for equal opportunity. She'd been rightly praised for her role in convicting the Skaf brothers and Dolly Dunn.

The premier consulted his Attorney-General, Greg Smith, before Cunneen was appointed. Smith had known Cunneen since their days together at the DPP. Back then Smith was president of the St Thomas More Society, the fraternity of Catholic judges, barristers and solicitors responsible for the Catholic Church's Red Mass. The government now considered Cunneen the most appropriate person to preside over an inquiry into police and the Church.

•

Asked my reaction to the premier's announcement, I expressed disappointment. Its terms of reference sounded suspiciously narrow and didn't look at the bigger picture. It had become clear Premier O'Farrell wouldn't support a Child Abuse Royal Commission, so I now looked to the federal government.

The phone calls didn't stop until our mobile batteries died. Driving home, we stopped for more interviews. When we arrived, we had three phones ringing simultaneously. News helicopters landed in our neighbour's yard, much to the amusement of the neighbourhood kids. Steve and Lisa were happy to have their lawn converted to a helipad. Married by Father Jim Fletcher, they were horrified when the truth about him emerged. Like most Australians, they supported a Child Abuse Royal Commission.

When we finally got a chance, I played our answering machine. It was full of messages from former police, all praising my interview, while many of those at work resented what I had done. Policing really is an odd culture. I heard from former police I hadn't spoken to for years. Reg Dowton called; he'd been one of my mentors at Central Police Station back in the 1970s. Then Rick Kane, my retired superintendent from Maitland. No sooner did I play his message than he called again. 'Well done, my boy,' he said. 'That took a lot of guts and I take my hat off to you. I'm proud of what you've done. Those bastards need to be exposed. Now, one bit of advice: watch your back! I mean it. Watch your back. I know what these bastards are like.'

Penny remarked on how most former police ended their call with the same words: 'Watch your back.'

I didn't need to be told. Despite the Police Royal Commission, I knew the Brotherhood was still alive and well.

The calls didn't stop over the weekend. Penny acted as my secretary, scheduling the media and booking interviews. The media were the key and were right behind us. It seemed they too realised the Cunneen Inquiry was hollow. Nothing less than a Child Abuse Royal Commission would do. Prime Minister Julia Gillard would later remark, 'The public call for a national Royal Commission became deafening.'

Between calls, I kept an eye on the political manoeuvring. When federal independents Tony Windsor and Nick Xenophon got behind a Child Abuse Royal Commission, it was game on. Word was that many government Labor Party backbenchers were supporting a Royal Commission, but not yet going public. Support also came from unexpected quarters when my local Labor Party MP, Joel Fitzgibbon, jumped on board. A former student of Catholic schools in Cessnock and Maitland where abuse had occurred, he later emailed me: 'You would know that I would not have spoken out without confirming with those who should know that you are a person worthy of my backing. I'm pleased to be able to say that you are very well respected out there.'

Opposition leader Tony Abbott, a close friend of Cardinal Pell, surprised everyone when he too backed a Royal Commission, provided it didn't just examine the Catholic Church. I suspected a lot more was happening behind the scenes.

Liberal and Labor ministers Joe Hockey and Bill Shorten put their differences aside in opposing a Royal Commission. Hockey said it would only re-traumatise victims, while Shorten said he wasn't sure it was the best way.

I kept up the pressure, doing as much media as I could. When Brisbane's *Courier Mail* pointed out I had already achieved a Special Commission, I said it wasn't enough and I wouldn't stop until we had a Royal Commission.

Prime Minister Gillard remained quiet, no doubt speaking to advisors and counting the numbers. When former prime ministers Kevin Rudd and Malcolm Fraser threw their support behind a Royal Commission, the balance swung. More politicians jumped on board. The media was in a frenzy as public support was polled at 95 percent.

That weekend and Monday were a blur of phone calls and interviews. Photographers turned up, one after the other. TV crews set up inside our home and out. I poured every spare minute and ounce of energy into it. While Penny baked date scones and made coffee for reporters, our aging fox terrier, Pebbles, managed to sneak into most photographs.

When I heard that Prime Minister Julia Gillard was about to make an announcement, I tried not to get my hopes up. I was doing a live phone interview for radio station Triple-J as Julia Gillard announced the Child Abuse Royal Commission. I wanted to hang up. Penny burst into tears. Relief and joy were mixed in a whirlwind of emotion. Phones rang, but we ignored them for the time being. We wanted to savour the moment. Steve and Lisa were the icing on our cake, appearing at our back door with beers and a bottle of champagne.

'Congratulations, Foxy.'

After years, decades, of campaigning for many, and four days after my ABC-TV interview, a Child Abuse Royal Commission was happening.

CHAPTER 24

AVOIDING DUPLICATION

With the announcement of a Child Abuse Royal Commission, many expected Premier O'Farrell to abandon the now superfluous Cunneen Inquiry. Doing so would avoid a smaller inquiry, not to mention save the state a tidy sum. If that happened I probably wouldn't have felt the need to write this book, or if I did, the story would have ended somewhere about now.

Not everyone was critical of the need for the Cunneen Inquiry, with Cardinal Pell telling one reporter he was 'confident a NSW Commission of Inquiry into historic sex abuse claims against priests in the Hunter region would not expose any ongoing offending'.

Having never worked in the Hunter, he was incredibly confident of the Inquiry's outcome. Only months earlier Pell had received correspondence from Cardinal Levada in the Vatican who was concerned about events in the Hunter. Now Pell fired a personal shot I believe was aimed at me, accusing a senior NSW policeman of smearing him with the allegation that the Church obstructed investigations into child sex abuse claims against priests.

My prediction of simultaneously taking on the police, government and Church was materialising.

Premier O'Farrell pushed ahead with the Cunneen Inquiry, asserting there was no guarantee the matters I raised would otherwise be examined. The Child Abuse Royal Commission later showed it was prepared to examine matters like mine when former Victorian Detective Denis Ryan gave evidence, but that was no help to me at the time.

Senior police had stopped Denis investigating paedophile priest Monsignor John Day, directing Denis to surrender all abuse survivors' statements. Day died years later without ever being brought to justice while Denis was pushed from the police force.

Premier O'Farrell announced, 'While I am determined to avoid duplication between state and federal inquiries in this important area, New South Wales will proceed with our Special Commission of Inquiry.'

Much lay between the lines. Prime Minister Gillard needed the support of all states to give the Child Abuse Royal Commission maximum authority, later saying, 'Almost all premiers were helpful, but nervous about work being already done in their states being redone.'

Her use of *nervous* was an interesting choice. Did it mean she had to negotiate with some premiers and, if so, would the Child Abuse Royal Commission still be allowed to look into the matters I had raised? I began to feel a little isolated.

I wasn't sure I needed a lawyer until Barrister Mark Cohen offered his services pro bono, saying I needed protection under the *Public Interest Disclosures Act*. For this to happen, I had to have complained to an oversight authority prior to going public. Like most, I had never heard of the act, let alone ticked all the boxes. Before speaking out no one asks, *Is there an Act of Parliament to protect me?*

And who was I supposed to complain to? My past experience with oversight agencies didn't exactly fill me with confidence.

Following Prime Minster Gillard's announcement, I received hundreds of cards and letters from well-wishers. Most arrived via the media, although some were delivered by police. I later discovered other letters delivered to police went missing. Penny and I read some each evening. Nearly all were from strangers, people we had never met, including Catholic priests and serving police. They too wanted to see change. We were moved by their expressions of support. Letters from survivors of childhood sexual abuse were difficult to read. Many left a lump in my throat. A number expressed anger at Towards Healing, with one saying the Church protocol left him 'more isolated and traumatised than before'.

One letter stood out. In the mid-1980s the author was a child when I charged her stepfather with repeatedly raping her. When her mother stood with the abuser, I helped community services relocate her so her schooling could continue. After serving his sentence, her stepfather was deported back to Britain. Thirty years later she remembered me, recounting how I took her statement, offered words of comfort and drove her to and from the trial. Now a mother herself, she wanted to tell me she had survived, and appreciated what I had done. Knowing I made a difference felt good.

A former detective I had never met told me of interference when he investigated abuse at St Stanislaus' College in Bathurst. Another opened up about police failures when investigating an Anglican Church paedophile network in Newcastle. I later passed their details on to the Child Abuse Royal Commission.

Amid all this, I unexpectedly received phone calls and emails from Margaret Cunneen. She wanted to run her inquiry's terms of reference (TOR) past me. As I feared, they were dreadfully narrow and centred more on police than child abuse. Initially they covered most of what was raised in the ABC-TV *Lateline* program, but that was later narrowed. Asked if I was happy, I said I wasn't. The issue was broader, I told her, saying I would discuss it with my lawyer. I took the opportunity to remind her of the premier's commitment to widen the TOR if necessary. Ultimately, that never occurred.

I learned that a number of journalists continued to receive calls from people anonymously identifying themselves as police, urging them to run negative stories about me. Most journalists saw it for what it was, taking what was said no further than letting me know.

Nick Ralston from the *Sydney Morning Herald* contacted me after receiving similar calls. Nick had also spoken to a senior police officer, off the record, who raised the ugly domestic dispute I'd had to investigate, involving the PVO against a fellow officer. Asked if I wanted to comment, I told Nick I wasn't going to play their game. He wrote the article anyway. It was balanced with a few positives thrown in, but what caught my eye were the quotes. Grabbing copies of the threatening letters sent to Penny and me, words and phrases were virtually identical. Whoever Nick spoke to was almost certainly one of those behind the threats. By now they would have realised I wasn't returning to work, but they must have still been worried about something.

Commissioner Andrew Scipione assured me I would not be subject to disciplinary action and to let him know if there were any reprisals. After I advised him of the mischief being perpetrated through the media he replied, 'As per our previous

254

discussion, I take allegations of harassment and bullying very seriously.'

My complaint was allocated to Deputy Commissioner Dave Hudson, with whom I had once worked on a multiple murder investigation. The police minister, premier's office and Margaret Cunneen were also informed of the threats made against me.

I won't go through it all, there's too much, but I will mention one incident I think encapsulates the ostracism to which I was subjected.

In early December 2012, Penny and I caught up with Justin and Kath Devonshire. I had worked with Justin for the best part of two decades. A committed detective sergeant, he had left the police force in 2006. When he suggested an evening out, I jumped at his offer.

We were enjoying our meal when twenty or so individuals filed past from behind me and sat with their partners. Justin and I recognised many. Most were now commissioned police officers. I guessed it was their Christmas social night out. Glances and whispers behind cupped hands. Heads nodded in our direction with a few spying looks. I had never had a falling out with any, quite the contrary, but not one made an effort to acknowledge me.

'Just ignore them, Foxy,' Justin advised.

We had half-finished our meal when they called for their bill.

'Hope the bastards get indigestion,' Justin remarked, before pointing out, 'Well, they now have to walk out past you.'

I intended looking each in the eye, wondering if any would have the decency to acknowledge me.

After sorting their bill, the waiter returned with a key. Getting quickly to their feet, they silently filed out the rear door. Mouth agape, Justin exclaimed, 'What a pack of fucking cowards!'

Two police remained. Once the rear door was locked they wandered over. One shook my hand before saying, 'I just want you to know I agree with most of what you said, Foxy. Good luck with everything.'

They didn't linger, and as Penny pointed out, 'They didn't say that in front of the others.'

'No, Pen, but at least they said it.'

Justin explained it. 'If they said that in front of the others their lives at work would be hell. I know you don't get it, anyone outside the job doesn't, but that's just the way it is. Now, let's forget it and go to the pub.'

And that's what we did.

On the positive side, I received an email from Chrissie Foster, the mother of the two little girls sexually abused in Melbourne and author of the book loaned to me by our neighbour: 'I thank you, Anthony thanks you and many who will never meet or tell you will also thank and admire you.'

Weeks later I got to meet Chrissie and Anthony at Pat's book launch. They were as warm as I had imagined.

As the year drew to a close, media attention waned. The Cunneen Inquiry intended holding a directions hearing as early as January, resulting in my Christmas and New Year becoming a blur of activity.

Greg Willis was a former police prosecutor turned solicitor. He joined Mark on my legal team. None of us had worked together before. I was under no illusions about going up against the police force and Church legal teams, we knew we had our work cut out. Mark guessed I might be in the witness box for two or three days. Anyone who has been in a witness box for five minutes knows what an ordeal it can be.

My medical discharge from the police force dragged on through this time. Although I never went to work, I remained a police officer until after the Cunneen Inquiry was complete. I spent my days working on my affidavit. I had saved a lot of paperwork, but I was nevertheless disadvantaged in not having access to police systems, work emails and correspondence I had left behind. I did the best I could.

Meanwhile, finding the right person to head the Child Abuse Royal Commission didn't happen overnight. It took two months of careful deliberation before Justice Peter McClellan, a judge of the New South Wales Court of Criminal Appeal, with a wealth of experience in previous government commissions, was announced in January 2013.

As we moved into February, the Cunneen Inquiry finished its directions hearing and issued me with subpoenas. After excluding much of the material from my ABC-TV *Lateline* interview, the Inquiry now unexpectedly expanded its TOR to include James Fletcher. It came as a complete surprise to me considering Lantle had ignored all my earlier urgings to examine Fletcher more fully.

My affidavit for the Cunneen Inquiry was over a hundred pages with two binders full of annexures. There was much legal to-ing and fro-ing as the Cunneen Inquiry issued an order prohibiting me from publicly discussing any of my evidence.

Before getting underway, the Cunneen Inquiry held closed sessions. On 7 February 2013, the doors were shut as I was led to the witness box. Counsel assisting the Inquiry, Julia Lonergan, with her fiery red hair, had earned the esteemed title Senior Counsel (SC). She liked to ask questions peering over the top of her glasses. I lost count of the times she extended the palm of her hand and said, 'I'm going to stop you there.'

I remember thinking she would have made a good traffic cop.

The initial closed hearing didn't take long to get ugly, with Julia Lonergan putting it to me that I was a liar, and Commissioner Cunneen dismissing Mark's objections.

I was called to further closed hearings in March and April, with me sitting in the witness box as late as 6 p.m. They were long, arduous days. After three days of closed hearings I had already passed Mark's prediction of how long I would be cross-examined before the public hearings even began.

From my position in the witness box, it felt like the Cunneen Inquiry was more intent on examining me than the issues I had raised. I no longer felt like a witness, but an accused.

One piece of evidence I was pleased to see was an email I sent Joanne McCarthy the evening of the Waratah meeting. After returning to Raymond Terrace, I had detailed the meeting in my diary, the same diary that later mysteriously disappeared. Fortunately, I had kept a report concerning the diary's disappearance, negating any suggestion it was a convenient invention. I had typed the email to Joanne using my diary notes. The importance of this email wasn't lost on me. I knew what occurred at the meeting would boil down to my word against half a dozen police. I had little doubt our recollections would differ. The email I sent Joanne corroborated what I said.

As the hearings continued, I became more frustrated by what was being disallowed. The narrowness of the TOR and what I saw as perplexing decisions distorted much of what I wanted to say. I had seen many legal processes, but what was occurring here alarmed me. I was told departmental convictions of a fellow officer weren't relevant. All reference of it was removed from my affidavit with instruction not to raise it. Not relevant? Surely this mattered when the officer had departmental convictions involving another serial child abuse investigation.

Eventually I'd had enough. Seeing what was happening, I had to vent. I told the Cunneen Inquiry it wasn't examining the issues I raised. I said much more at this closed hearing concerning evidence being removed from my affidavit. For legal reasons I am prevented from publishing what I said, so I cannot repeat it here.

I now understood where I sat and wondered whether the NSW Government pushed ahead with the Cunneen Inquiry so the Royal Commission wouldn't be re-examining issues it looked at.

My affidavit explained that separating my evidence into different hearings – sending bits to the Child Abuse Royal Commission and removing other parts altogether – distorted the true picture. If the Cunneen Inquiry wanted to get to the bottom of what really happened, it couldn't keep dissecting my evidence. I pointed out if my evidence was constrained it would undermine the Inquiry, adding if the TOR needed amending, it needed to happen sooner rather than later. It didn't.

There are often good legal reasons evidence is disallowed, but what was being removed here made no sense to me. I know some might say: *Peter Fox was discredited by the Cunneen Inquiry, why wouldn't he say that?*

I don't dispute I am subjective. All I can do is set out some of what I can legally say occured as I saw it, and let you judge.

In addition to Fletcher and McAlinden, my affidavit listed other Hunter clergy who had abused children. Because they fell outside the TOR, however, any mention of them or their crimes was redacted (the legal term for 'removed').

Tony Jones had asked, 'How does this much evil get concentrated in one small area?'

His question couldn't be answered by examining just two priests. Investigating patterns of behaviour needs a holistic approach. By looking at cases in isolation, the terms of reference forced the Cunneen Inquiry to do exactly the same as the police had done up until that point.

In early April 2013, prior to my third closed hearing, I located notes I had written about Denis McAlinden. They included seven blind-reported intelligence numbers assigned to each report showing the Church had knowledge of McAlinden's crimes dating back to 1951.

Two months earlier, in February 2013, Suzie Smith had run a story, 'Conflict of Interest in Towards Healing' about a police officer sitting on a Church board. It sounded to me like an extension of blind reporting. After discussion with my barrister, Mark Cohen, I provided the Cunneen Inquiry with a five-page supplementary statement. Included were my notes and Nicholas Cowdery's comment: 'This process could be viewed as the Church conscripting the police force into its own agenda.'

With the intelligence relating to McAlinden, it had to all fall within the Cunneen Inquiry's TOR, I thought. One of the blind reports related directly to the child sexual abuse of one of McAlinden's nieces, Denise, a key witness at the centre of the Lantle investigation. To my dismay, it too was excluded.

CHAPTER 25

THE WHOLE TRUTH, AND NOTHING BUT

The Cunneen Inquiry separated its hearings. The first, involving police, was set for May; the Church component would take place in July. Indications were I would be questioned for a further two days during each. That would be seven days in total. I wasn't looking forward to it. Just before 6 p.m. after my third full day of evidence before the closed hearings, Commissioner Cunneen conceded it was 'yet another marathon performance'. I didn't then realise that a lot worse was to come.

All parties received subpoenas to produce everything relating to the TOR. My emails to Joanne McCarthy would show I ignored the direction to not speak to her after the meeting. I knew the police force would use this against me, but I was determined to produce everything. During the domestic dispute case, I was asked in an interview if I had contacted journalist Joanne McCarthy. I was under no illusions I would be criticised for saying no, when in fact I had kept in contact with Joanne throughout that time, and that was fair enough. By laying everything on the table I was bound to have some bark knocked off me. I would take that on the chin. The bigger picture was what mattered to me.

When I was directed to hand everything over to Strike Force Lantle, I feared statements might go missing. I hadn't spoken to Barbara in years, but I had a clear recollection of taking her statement; of her sitting beside me reading the screen as I typed for hours until the statement met with her approval. Barbara had told her story to Joanne McCarthy before she spoke to me, and when I handed Barbara her statement she told me Joanne had asked for a copy. Joanne and Barbara hadn't been able to meet, so when Joanne asked me, I provided it. It was an error. I should have let Barbara give it to Joanne herself. I knew I would be criticised for that too.

At the Cunneen Inquiry I wasn't allowed to see Barbara give evidence. Lantle had taken a new statement, with Barbara now rejecting everything in her original. Before I gave evidence I learned that Barbara had changed her mind again, now saying that most of her original statement was true. What I do know is that Barbara read her original statement that I typed many times; she even took it home to make corrections, which I would then include in our next session. Every word was hers, if not she would never have signed it. I don't know what occurred after Lantle's involvement. All I can say is I hid nothing during the Inquiry, good or bad, but as you will read, not everyone played by the same rules.

•

A Special Commission of Inquiry is supposed to be just that: an inquiry. In the case of the Cunneen Inquiry, however, I felt like a criminal on trial. Julia Lonergan led my evidence carefully, ever so carefully avoiding material from my affidavit that was deemed inadmissible. I had sworn an oath, to tell the truth, the whole truth and nothing but the truth. Trouble was, the whole truth wasn't allowed. Despite Commissioner Cunneen announcing that some redacted material would be forwarded to the Child Abuse Royal Commission and other inquiries, it wouldn't help me now. Police affidavits were tendered without question. Pleas for what was left of my affidavit to be similarly tendered were ignored. No one got to see the extensive swathes of blanked-out evidence.

Nor was I permitted to be present when certain witnesses gave evidence, despite some of their evidence relating to me. This meant, I couldn't advise my legal counsel as the evidence unfolded. I was particularly frustrated when even my lawyers weren't present for Denise's and Anthea's evidence.

Two days in the witness box became three, then four and eventually a week. On top of the three days I had endured at the closed hearings, it was mind-numbing. It seemed the Inquiry tried to trip me up on answers I had given months earlier. A memory test. After eight days in the witness box I must have set some sort of record. Others weren't subjected to anywhere near the same scrutiny.

Penny and I started our days at six. The drive from Branxton to Newcastle where the public hearings were being held took from ninety minutes to two hours depending on traffic prior to the Hunter Expressway's completion. We would meet Mark Cohen and Greg Willis at eight or nine o'clock, then it was into the witness box. By the time we got home through peak-hour traffic it was dark. I would read material in the car and continue after we got home. While Penny prepared dinner I would field calls from Mark as he read transcripts. Then there was preparation for the next day. More than once I fell asleep in my chair. It's amazing how mental exhaustion fatigues as much as physical hard work. This went on throughout the Inquiry, even between and after my evidence. I felt drained as there seemed no end in sight.

After leading my evidence, Julia Lonergan would cross-examine me. A team of police lawyers followed, taking turns. It wasn't just one or two questions, it went on for days, relentlessly. I would be exhausted before morning tea, continuing until lunch and then into the afternoon. The usual adjournment time was often ignored; I just had to keep going.

When police finished cross-examining me it was the Church's turn. There wasn't just one lawyer or legal team. After the Diocese's barrister had finished came lawyers for individual bishops and priests. Sitting in the witness box facing one lawyer after another was like being in a tag-team fight, except I had no one to tag. As each lawyer exhausted their questions they passed the attack on to the next. I had never been subjected to anything like this, nor had I witnessed or heard of anything like it. In my police career, even during complex murder trials I was only ever cross-examined for a day or two at most. The manner of questioning at the Cunneen Inquiry was, in my experience, well beyond the norm, with aggression often unrestrained. Oppressive and bullying are words that come to mind.

My cross-examination often left Penny, Joanne McCarthy, Suzie Smith and others in tears. Joanne later told the ABC-TV's Andrew Dodd, 'It was like sitting in a playground watching a kid being bullied and being powerless to do anything about it.'

I sat there, head throbbing, mind dazed, facing one interrogation after the next, determined not to give in.

At one point, Wayne Roser SC, barrister for police, pushed a little too hard, wanting to know to whom I referred in an email as 'pricks'. I singled out an officer's name. I wasn't allowed to explain why, because the Cunneen Inquiry had already redacted the reason. When pushed, I had no choice but to say, and my answer was struck from the record. I cannot now repeat what I said for fear of legal repercussions. The Cunneen Inquiry nevertheless cited my characterisation of this officer in its final report, but omitted the reason I referred to him in that manner. It was selective and, in my view, unfair. The police force knew the whole truth. If the big picture was exposed, it would seriously damage public confidence, not just in the police force, but leadership of the entire Lantle investigation.

The attacks weren't just coming in court. Much appeared to me to be going on behind the scenes. A journalist for the *Australian* newspaper was writing articles critical of me. I soon learned to stay clear of him. Then one day after the hearings had commenced, my solicitor, Greg Willis, saw the journalist sitting at the back of a local cafe in conversation with a senior police officer who was a witness in the proceedings. The next day, the journalist published another story critical of me. In the meantime, in the Inquiry, I was continually being attacked for having kept my contact with journalist Joanne McCarthy a secret. The same rules seemingly didn't apply to all.

•

Former and current police, some I investigated for misconduct, attended the inquiry. A former officer I will refer to as Basil (not his real name) was 'old school', one of those I believed for years was part of the 'boys' club' that existed in the Hunter. To my mind, Basil believed in loyalty; if you wore a police uniform, nothing else mattered. He turned up at court hearings supporting the officer charged with the pepper-spraying of the

Aboriginal boy, and again for the officer who faced the PVO hearing. It therefore didn't surprise me when he turned up at the Cunneen Inquiry.

On my third day of public evidence Basil didn't sit with his friends; instead he moved to the opposite side of the court to sit behind Penny and Pat Feenan. I politely asked if he could sit elsewhere.

'Get stuffed,' was his venomous reply. Called to the witness box I was about to be sworn in when Basil started pulling on the back of Penny and Pat's seat. Having gained my attention, he smirked. Penny and Pat were both worried by his behaviour. No doubt seeing the concern in my face, Julia Lonergan approached me to find out what was wrong. Penny's distress confirmed to her that something was amiss. Explaining, I expected Basil to be moved. Instead, Julia Lonergan moved a single chair forward of the public gallery and asked Penny, now all but in tears, to sit there. Now a spectacle, Penny sat in the middle of the court more frightened than before. I was disgusted. No one from the Inquiry approached Basil. He remained where he was, delighting in his mischief. Penny was made to feel like she had done something wrong. I wanted to get up to hug her, but the Inquiry resumed as if nothing had happened. I now regret not ignoring the formalities. Not a word was said about this intimidatory incident. At the morning adjournment I made clear what was happening. To my knowledge, nothing more was done.

During the break Basil and another former police officer walked behind Penny and me, breathing down our necks. Through the foyer, down the steps, along the footpath, even across the road, they remained on our heels. The presence of friends on the far corner forced them to move off.

As the Inquiry continued, Penny was isolated from her support while this man stayed where he was, glaring at me from the back of the court. I organised for Penny to be seated at the side of the court with Dave Woolnough. As I have mentioned from my early days at Cessnock, Dave was a friend and former detective; he was also groomsman at our wedding, thirty-odd years before. I am indebted for his unwavering support in shielding Penny. Penny shed tears but somehow held it together.

The intimidation had an impact on us both. The Cunneen Inquiry seemed loath to take action or comment publicly. While the intimidation continued, I was expected to keep giving evidence as if nothing was happening.

This was entirely different treatment to that given to another witness, one from the Church, who claimed he was being harangued outside the court. Father Bill Burston was one of the priests who visited James Fletcher at Branxton when my investigation first began. Back in 1974, Burston was one of the first to arrive at the Newcastle home of thirteen-year-old clergy abuse victim Andrew Nash, the night the boy hanged himself. Frustrated, Andrew's brother confronted Burston outside the Cunneen Inquiry, telling Burston to tell the truth when giving evidence. The Cunneen Inquiry had already determined it would not examine Andrew's suicide. In contrast with the handling of my situation, Commissioner Cunneen stopped proceedings to give the public gallery a good dressing down and excused the priest from giving evidence until he got over his upset.

I had no such reprieve. When I left the court for a toilet break, Basil followed a few paces behind. He didn't care about being captured on the court security camera. Why would he – no one had pulled him up thus far. Standing at the urinal, there was plenty of spare room. Basil wasn't interested, he just stood behind me, arms folded, endeavouring to intimidate. After I washed my hands, he followed me back to court without availing himself of the facilities. On it went. No one did or said anything.

•

Mark handed my complaint to the Cunneen Inquiry detailing the ongoing harassment. Nothing changed. The rigorous cross-examinations continued.

Basil appeared again at the next hearings in July. Again my cross-examination was relentless. Even though the police component was finished, police lawyers turned up for another go. Wayne Roser was tough, but professional. By now he had ceased representing the NSW Police Force and his position was filled by Patrick Saidi, whose manner I can only describe as hostile.

In July I had a bad case of the flu. I shouldn't have turned up, but I believed in telling the truth, so far as the Inquiry permitted, and didn't want to be seen as surrendering. I took flu tablets, stacked tissues in the witness box and persevered. The cross-examination was unyielding. Saidi's methods were amplified when he was provided with a platform directly in front of the witness box. My barrister, Mark Cohen, objected as Saidi's manner escalated to a point where even the public gallery began reacting, and Julia Lonergan was forced to intervene. There was no real sanction. Saidi reverted to his hostile questioning until the next objection. No transcript can convey his demeanour.

Pat Feenan was there supporting Penny and me. Where she got her strength I will never know, but I will be eternally grateful for the steadfast way she held Penny's hand and shared words of comfort. I cannot speak of her highly enough.

Walking to the hearings one morning, Penny rhetorically asked when it would all end. I must have looked very down.

'My darling Irish mother used to have a saying,' Pat said as she turned to me. 'Just keep walking towards thunder.'

Having never heard the expression, I asked what it meant.

'No matter how dark the clouds, bright the lightning or loud the roar of thunder, don't be afraid of the trouble ahead, keep walking and face up to it. Eventually the storm will pass, and you will emerge in the sun.'

I smiled. 'I'll remember that. Your mum was a wise lady.'

As the days wore on, I counted nine, ten, eleven days in the witness box, and still no reprieve. I remember thinking: *Are they allowed to do this? Isn't there a law about how long this can continue?* My medication for PTSD and stress had already been increased. As we reached Friday, I prayed it would end. Lawyers continued taking it in turns. Julia Lonergan would resume her cross-examination at the start, the end, or whenever she needed. There it was again, the traffic cop, her hand in my face: 'I'm going to stop you there.'

Breathing became difficult as my mind started to shut down. Staring at the ceiling, I was sure I could see the sky. I was numb, willing myself somewhere else. Perhaps that's how your mind works when it's completely exhausted – it just takes you somewhere, anywhere, a subconscious escape. Friends said they were worried about me. Did I look at the clock? I don't remember. I knew the day had to end sometime. The week would come to a close and it would stop. Then they said they wanted me back in the witness box on Monday. Was it now eleven or twelve days? I'd lost count.

I went home feeling completely sapped. As she watched me collapse in my chair, Penny began crying, then sobbed. She begged me not to go back.

'You can see Dr Morris. You can't take any more of this, you were like a zombie today. If you go back, I'm frightened I'll lose you.'

I didn't say anything. My mind was too numb. I just wanted to rest.

Over the weekend I pulled myself somewhat back together. Maybe it was pride, dogged determination or just sheer stupidity. Like a punch-drunk boxer, I staggered back for round thirteen.

I don't remember much about that day. Pat said I continued to look at the ceiling, to the point where sometime during the morning Julia Lonergan asked why I was looking up, and I gave some lame excuse. I didn't realise how debilitated I had become. I was hearing questions, but apparently my answers were all over the place. Even now I don't fully remember what I said. I had been pushed to the end of my endurance. Still the questions came, hammered home with answers demanded. Towards the end of that day Julia Lonergan chastised, 'I didn't want you to look upwards. I want you to look at your statement.'

I could only say, 'Sorry.'

On and on it went.

I didn't see Penny leave. The intimidation, and unremitting cross-examination had become too much. I later learned she went to Pat's sister's house, where she broke down in her arms. Fortunately this was my last day. On the ropes, the normal adjournment time came and went, but the bell didn't sound. Julia Lonergan launched into a new spate of questioning for nearly an hour, until it was finally over.

Penny had been a tremendous support, but emotionally she could take no more. I had no choice; I was required for the rest of the Inquiry, though fortunately not in the witness box. Penny stayed home. She'd had enough.

In late July, a birthday for Lisa, our neighbour, was organised at a Maitland Hotel. I told Penny I would meet her there after the day's hearing. Arriving early, I went to the function room alone and waited.

Security video would later show Basil skulking about the hotel, banging outside a window to get my attention. He yelled and jumped about, but I couldn't hear him through the glass. I looked away, hoping he would get the message and leave. He didn't. Minutes later Basil walked inside; hotel staff would later corroborate seeing him there. Leaning in the doorway, he threatened me, then left.

I wrote down his threats and rang police. My statement recorded him saying: 'This is where you are hiding, you fucking liar. You will get yours trying to destroy people's reputations. One day when you are not expecting it, it will just be you and me and I am going to take you apart, you cunt.'

I didn't react beyond telling him to go away.

As he scurried off, Basil yelled, 'Your day will come when you are not expecting it.'

As luck would have it, I saw a family I knew. They had seen Basil. Although they did not hear everything he said, they thought his behaviour odd.

Reluctant to get involved, police told me to take my own civil action. I stood my ground. Eventually police issued an interim violence order. Basil consented to the order and conditions without the case going to a hearing on the proviso there be no criminal charges. If I pursued criminal charges Penny would have to testify, and she was in no condition to do that. Basil's threatening behaviour had already resulted in Penny seeing our doctor, being prescribed medication and referred for counselling. Although police again offered to pay, Penny refused. She wanted nothing to do with them.

I notified the Cunneen Inquiry of the violence order requiring Basil not to 'assault, molest, harass, threaten or otherwise interfere' with me or my family. Still he continued to turn up, and in spite of everything, it was explained to me by a senior officer of the inquiry that Basil was entitled to be there.

By the time the Cunneen Inquiry concluded, Penny and I were exhausted, lacking any semblance of motivation or energy. We had been through an experience worse than anything we had imagined. Cynthia Kardell, president of Whistleblowers Australia, had warned me it was normal to praise the message and kill the messenger. She had seen it all before. Indications were, from the manner of my cross-examination and questions asked, the Cunneen Inquiry would come down hard on me, but after thirteen days of relentless cross-examination, I was so numb, I didn't care. It was over.

CHAPTER 26

AMBUSHED

Chrissie and Anthony Foster had followed everything via the media. That's when Chrissie called, inviting Penny and me to spend time with them at their Gippsland cottage. I don't know what made me say yes. I don't normally accept invitations on the spot. Perhaps I appreciated that we needed a break. Penny felt awkward; having never met Chrissie and Anthony, she thought we would be imposing.

As our tyres crunched on the gravel, Chrissie and Anthony came out to meet us. I have lost count of the times Penny remarked how welcome she felt from the moment we arrived. Chrissie greeted us with a huge smile and hug. Anthony smiled just as broadly as he shook my hand. Thereafter, a mere handshake was never enough, we would embrace like life-long friends. It was a week we will never forget. Chrissie and Anthony refused to allow us to do anything.

'You're our guests,' was the constant refrain.

We would all stroll the gardens and adjoining forest, looking at the wildlife and taking in the crisp mountain air. Chrissie and Anthony delighted in chaperoning our first trip to Melbourne. They loved showing it off as much as we loved seeing it. We instantly fell in love with the city, its cafes and trams, the Flinders Street Station facade, the quaint laneways with their mix of old and new, and, of course, its people.

Evenings were spent around a fire with a glass of red wine. Anthony and I had a couple of late nights in deep conversation. He was worried about Penny and me, and wanted to know how we were. I told him I believed the Cunneen Inquiry would be damning of me and find much of what I said to be untrue. Anthony put his wine down and looked at me seriously.

'You had nothing to gain, Pete. We've seen it all before. I believe every word you said and so do thousands of others, and that won't change.'

Anthony then said something profound. 'When abused kids tried to tell their story, no one believed them either.'

We discussed more as Anthony assured me the impact of the Cunneen Inquiry would fade as the national Child Sexual Abuse Royal Commission got underway. He was right. That's when he urged me to write this story, saying what happened needed to be told.

•

In the four months since the Cunneen Inquiry, our health had improved. Penny and I travelled to Sydney for the Child Abuse Royal Commission.

Case Study Four was the first hearing to examine aspects of the Catholic Church's role in the child sexual abuse scandal. Its controversial Towards Healing protocol was now in the spotlight. We didn't know the survivors giving evidence, but we wanted them to know they were supported. Outside were other abuse survivors. Purple and yellow placards condemned the Catholic Church and other abusive institutions. Care

Leavers Australasia Network (CLAN) showed up wherever the Child Abuse Royal Commission sat. Arriving early, Penny and I were greeted by the group's president, Leonie Sheedy, before posing with CLAN members for photographs. Over time many would become familiar faces and friends.

The first survivor to give evidence was retired schoolteacher Joan Isaacs, whose sexual abuse by Brisbane priest, Frank Derriman, I first mentioned in chapter eight. She looked as nervous as anyone I had seen. Supported by her husband and sons, Joan was whisked into a private waiting room. No sooner had the door closed than her husband, Ian, re-emerged. We had never met, but he and Joan had recognised me. Joan wanted to shake my hand before giving evidence. I was humbled. We spoke only briefly that day, but I assured her that many were behind her. In giving evidence Joan radiated courage, paving the way for others to follow. Her evidence was strong, confident and damning of the Church in which she was raised. Joan lifted the veil from Towards Healing, exposing it for the abusive process it was. I thought of how police in Newcastle had praised the protocol, deferring to the Church by holding Towards Healing up as a viable alternative to the criminal justice system.

While having coffee with Chrissie Foster and Penny, I received calls from my barrister, Mark Cohen, informing me that the Cunneen Inquiry hadn't finished with me, and was now demanding documents I didn't have. A few calls later I was told the Inquiry wanted me to travel home and search for them. Explaining we were in Sydney at the Royal Commission didn't change the Inquiry's mind. I ended up contacting our daughter-in-law, who looked through my files and confirmed no such documents existed.

Later we met with Dr Cathy Kezelman, president of the child abuse advocacy group, Blue Knot Foundation, of which

Chrissie, Anthony and I were ambassadors. Cathy had asked me to become an ambassador earlier in the year, when her foundation presented me with an award for 'outstanding pursuit of justice and outstanding commitment to survivors of child abuse'. Mark called again. The Cunneen Inquiry wanted me back in the witness box. A subpoena served on me earlier in the year was still in effect, so I couldn't refuse. My stomach churned.

'When?'

'Tomorrow.'

I had thought it was over, now my nightmares returned. The call darkened what had been an inspiring day.

Soon after, I received a more upsetting call from one of my sisters. Our brother had just been rushed to Liverpool Hospital in a serious condition. Working under a truck, it had rolled and dragged him, tearing his arm around the drive shaft. Apologising, I left Penny with friends and caught a train to Liverpool Hospital.

It was after 2 a.m. when I arrived back at our hotel. Assured my brother's injuries, although serious, were not life-threatening, I managed to grab a few hours' sleep before attending the Royal Commission. My family phoned with regular updates. I had been instructed to be at the Cunneen Inquiry's Sydney hearing rooms no later than 1 p.m. Expecting to be finished by early afternoon, I told my family I would see them later at the hospital.

We arrived at the Cunneen Inquiry early. Mark had little idea what this was about other than the Inquiry wanted to ask further questions about James Fletcher's companion, Des Harrigan. Mark placed on record my mental state, family tragedy and lack of sleep. Emma Sullivan, who was assisting the Inquiry, told me I didn't look well. Asking how long I would be in the witness box, she replied, 'Not long.'

I pushed for something more definite. 'How long is not long? Twenty minutes?'

Her reply: 'If that.'

It left enough time to get a train to the hospital before visiting hours ended.

I was surprised so many media were informed and attended at such short notice. Patrick Saidi was there with detectives Jeff Little and Paul Jacob. I had been told it was the Cunneen Inquiry that had questions. I now suspected something else was planned.

Julia Lonergan began by asking benign questions about Des Harrigan, making me think, *You got me here for this?*

The longer she went, the more she digressed. It didn't take long for twenty minutes to pass. Then it was Patrick Saidi's turn. His manner was little different to months before. He attacked me over an intelligence report I submitted following Fletcher's failed appeal in 2006. Mark protested, calling it an ambush. There was no notification of police cross-examination, nor were we given notice about the intelligence report. Police had the report all along and should have dealt with it months ago. Now it was being used to drag me back for a separate hearing. Commissioner Cunneen dismissed Mark's objections.

Anxious for it to end, I kept looking at the clock. By 3.30 p.m. I realised that Emma Sullivan's twenty minutes was far from accurate. There was no hurry. Saidi's bluster centred on me classifying the intelligence report as A1, which meant highly reliable. Saidi didn't believe the content of the report should have been classified that high. It seemed trivial and I really didn't care. The whole issue seemed pedantic. He ran out of steam when I explained I didn't create the classification, it was computer generated. The knowledge of police instructing him was wanting, bringing Saidi's line of questioning to an abrupt halt. Was this the reason for dragging me back?

Julia Lonergan looked tired. On and on it went until she looked at her watch. Yes, it was late. Grabbing her bag, she packed up and left. I would have liked to have done the same, but others weren't finished with me.

When the Child Abuse Royal Commission concluded for the day, Chrissie arrived at the Cuneen Inquiry to sit with Penny, but was unable to get in. The building had been closed.

People headed home as Emma Sullivan spoke with police outside as documents changed hands.

A court doesn't normally sit more than two hours in one stretch. By 5.45 p.m. I had been cross-examined for over four hours, despite the Cunneen Inquiry's knowledge of my circumstances. When Saidi again raised my writing a book, I realised Anthony was right. I told Saidi I had not written anything about the Church. I even offered my computer hard drive for checking. Saidi wasn't interested, he simply rehashed ground already gone over months before. It dragged on. In Lonergan's absence, it seemed junior staff were given practice cross-examining me, including Emma Sullivan, who had assured me my cross-examination would only be twenty minutes, *if that*.

Half-past six came and went with no end in sight. It had now been more than five hours. There seemed no purpose as we continually went over old ground. No refreshment breaks, it just went on and on and on. I realised I wouldn't get to the hospital to see my brother before 8 p.m., when visiting ceased. Margaret Cunneen had placed my family circumstances on record, so it wasn't as if they didn't know. I had already started looking at the ceiling. With the help of friends and health professionals, I had been nursed back to health. Now

I felt myself spiralling again, close to collapse. It finally ended around 7 p.m.

My family was upset, as was I. I told Penny I didn't feel well. I wanted to go home. There was no argument. We grabbed our things and walked to Wynyard Railway Station. It was all silent on the short train trip back to our car. I remember driving along the expressway and thinking, *What next?* Couldn't they just write their bloody report, damn me and be done with it? What were they were trying to achieve? I had thought eight days was some sort of record, now my cross-examination had reached fourteen. Nearly three weeks of hearing days. You could run a murder trial in the time I had been in the witness box. My head was thumping. This was why no one spoke out. Was this my punishment and a message for anyone else who might consider doing the same? It felt like it.

I sensed the blood drain as I struggled to focus. My head was dizzy as the colours faded around me. The car drifted as I began to black out. Penny yelled, grabbing me and the steering wheel. I remember stepping on the brake pedal, screeching the tyres as we slewed towards the barrier. Somehow we managed to bring the car to a halt just past the Hawkesbury Bridge.

Penny sobbed. 'They've broken you. I hope the bastards are happy. They've finally got what they wanted.'

We embraced and cried as the traffic rushed past. The following morning, my doctor and psychologist wrote to the Inquiry saying I'd had enough.

CHAPTER 27

CONDEMNED, DISCREDITED AND SHAMED

The Royal Commission was in full swing. For the Catholic Church and other religious institutions, things weren't going well.

That's when Cardinal George Pell – the man Anthony Foster had described during the Victorian Parliamentary Inquiry as having a *'sociopathic lack of empathy'* – received his promotion to the Vatican. In the midst of the Church's worst turmoil, Australia's most senior Catholic was leaving. There was to be no fanfare. Cardinal Pell was merely taking up an appointment, that's all. Nonetheless, a few friends and supporters insisted on a send-off. In March 2014, as the Cunneen Inquiry completed its report, a discreet farewell was organised.

It may have been low-key, but the guest list was impressive. Premier Barry O'Farrell stood shoulder to shoulder with Cardinal Pell while his Attorney-General, Greg Smith, spoke in glowing praise of His Eminence. Premier O'Farrell, reportedly, didn't need notes, but spoke from the heart to express the greatest respect for the Cardinal and his Church.

'In Australian society the Church always gets priority and central position.' With that, the premier wished Cardinal Pell, 'Good luck, happy life with health, success and bright future.'

•

The Cunneen Inquiry completed its work. Parties receiving draft findings had to sign a confidentiality agreement. No one, under any circumstances, I was told, was to disclose the contents. Reading the draft, I sank into the depths of depression. As feared, I was to be condemned, discredited and shamed. It was nothing less than what I had expected; even so, it hurt. Cynthia Kardell had warned, 'It happens to all whistle-blowers.'

I found it impossible to get out of my chair. Unable to travel to Sydney, Mark Cohen stayed at our home overnight to prepare our response. It proved futile.

On 7 May I received a phone call from the journalist with *The Australian* newspaper who had written negative stories regarding me. I had already told him I would make no comment. Even so, our conversation was alarming.

I immediately emailed Mark, telling him what the journalist had said, 'I have been told this is what the Commission is likely to be going to find.'

To say I was astonished would be an understatement. Despite the Cunneen Inquiry's confidentiality agreement, someone had leaked the proposed findings. Mark immediately notified the Cunneen Inquiry. Intent on running his story the next day, the journalist asked for my comment on three of the findings: 'That I'd leaked information to journalist Joanne McCarthy; I hadn't been directed off the McAlinden case; and there was no Catholic Mafia.'

I certainly wasn't going to place myself at risk by commenting. The journalist ignored the hypocrisy of police doing the very thing for which I was being condemned. Suspecting who was behind the leaks, I told him I knew he protected his sources but that I wasn't a fool and knew who he had been talking to.

Caught off guard, it seemed to me the journalist tried to deflect. 'I want you to know, Peter, that I didn't get this from just one source … I had to check what I was told with others before I put this together.'

I scoffed. I probably ranted and I told him 'All I ever wanted was a Royal Commission to protect kids.' I told him that I wasn't impressed the findings had been leaked, and that the whole inquiry had too narrow a focus. The real story was the Royal Commission and that's what he should be focusing on.

He agreed. 'Yes, they were narrow, everyone thought that. The Royal Commission is a real success.'

I told him, 'Someone is using the findings for their own agenda. I am disappointed with the Commission and that they couldn't even ensure the findings were kept confidential.'

'You don't want me to say that, do you? It wasn't really the Commission's fault, but I'll put it in if you like.'

The Inquiry's confidentiality clause was again mocked when Sydney radio personality Ray Hadley read an anonymous letter revealing further material the next day. My barrister, Mark Cohen, called on the Cunneen Inquiry to use its coercive powers to question both the journalist and Ray Hadley. Julia Lonergan sent the following enigmatic reply: 'We have received instructions from the commissioner which are, as you would understand, confidential. In the circumstances, and given the privileged nature of the instructions, I cannot disclose anything further.'

Convoluted, mystifying, legalistic language. It said nothing. I wasn't asked for a statement about the leaks. If anything occurred, the Cunneen Inquiry ensured it remained privileged and confidential. The reputation of whoever leaked the information remained safe.

Before running his story, the *Australian* journalist contacted Dr Cathy Kezelman. In light of the leaked findings, he inquired if she would withdraw my ambassadorship of the Blue Knot Foundation. Cathy was disturbed at this attempt to sensationalise. Needless to say, he didn't get the response he was after.

Three months later, the same journalist invited me to coffee, saying I 'had every right to ask questions'.

It was a curious invitation. With little trust and nothing to be gained, I didn't reply.

•

Penny and I hadn't planned to be away when the final report was released, although it probably worked out for the best. I had things to say, but thought better of them. Blazed across the media, the Cunneen Inquiry's discrediting of me was complete.

I don't know who it was who reduced the negative findings about me to letter form before sending them to every mailbox in our street. Outraged, our neighbours notified police. Nothing ever came of it. In any case, the letters backfired. Recognising this childish mischief for what it was, neighbours rallied around us.

Like I said, I expected some criticism. But how did I get things so wrong as to deserve the degree of discredit levelled against me by the Cunneen Inquiry? Daniel Feenan said he thought the findings weren't balanced. A Government Special Commission of Inquiry costing millions of tax-payer dollars, staffed by some of the country's top lawyers – how could it not be balanced? The findings were there for all to read. But was anything omitted? Surely not. And if anything was, I'm sure it would have been for good legal reasons. At least that's what I used to tell myself. If I thought otherwise, what of it? The more I objected, the more it would have been viewed as sour grapes.

A Special Commission of Inquiry versus a now discredited cop. There was only ever going to be one winner.

As I walked Penny to a medical appointment in Maitland, an elderly woman approached us and said, 'Hold your head up, Peter Fox. You did the right thing. Everyone knows what was going on.'

Penny grabbed my arm. 'See, people are a lot smarter than you give them credit for.'

The *New Matilda* newspaper ran 'Breaking the Witness', which stated: 'As the Inquiry has unfolded it has become increasingly clear that it is not really the Catholic Church or the NSW Police that it is being put under the microscope. It is Peter Fox.'

•

I determined to keep my comments about the Cunneen Inquiry to myself, at least until Archbishop Wilson, who was later charged with concealing child sexual abuse, had his court case completed. (Wilson was found guilty at trial but after four months home detention, the conviction was overturned on appeal and he was acquitted.)

So, where to begin? I lived through it in minute detail, but you don't have to, so I will focus on the main findings. Like

I said, I know I'm subjective, but I will try to be as dispassionate as possible. You can read my account, at least the parts I can legally discuss, together with parts of the Cunneen Inquiry that are not subject to suppression orders, and decide for yourself.

Police emerged from the Cunneen Inquiry with reputations relatively intact. Some were hailed as heroes and a few clergy were criticised. Much of the blame for covering up clergy child sexual abuse was attributed to dead bishops. Nothing new there. A couple of elderly priests accepted early retirement and Premier O'Farrell trumpeted the Cunneen Inquiry's success by criticising Father Brian Lucas, before the Church moved him away from all the fuss. After spending millions of dollars, that was it. Some may have thought the discrediting of a bothersome detective to have been money well spent, but there were no nation-changing recommendations.

CHAPTER 28

THE CATHOLIC MAFIA

I don't want to drag out my concerns about the Cunneen Inquiry's findings, so I will confine it to those leaked to the previously mentioned journalist and a few others. The published story was threefold: one, that I had leaked information to journalist Joanne McCarthy; two, that I had not been directed off the McAlinden case as I stated; and, finally, that there was no Catholic Mafia.

Did I leak information to Joanne McCarthy? Joanne spoke to witnesses and survivors well before Lantle existed. She documented, listened to their stories and wrote articles. When the police force showed no interest, Joanne approached Shaun McLeod, then me. She relayed survivors' stories, arranged contact, supplied documents and emails. When new names arose, Joanne pointed me in the right direction. She already knew the story of each witness. So, what was being leaked?

Two officers were left red-faced after suggesting I leaked information concerning Father David O'Hearn to Joanne in 2008, when the source turned out to be a Church media release. The Cunneen Inquiry took the view that the incident was of 'insufficient relevance' to its terms of reference (which as I've previously noted, were very narrow).

Insufficient relevance? Rather than criticise police for jumping to wrong conclusions that potentially led to me being stopped from investigating Church matters, the Inquiry said no more.

Did I maintain contact with Joanne? The answer is yes, and I was prepared to be criticised for doing so. But still, what was leaked? Removed from the investigation and having no contact with witnesses, other than speaking to Anthea when she initially called me for help, I had no idea what Lantle was doing. Joanne and I shared concern about Lantle's stagnation, but was that leaking? When Joanne wrote her April 2011 article, it was suggested I was the source. The fact I had been off work for months didn't matter.

My use of the words 'Catholic Mafia'? I had volunteered the information about when I had first heard the term knowing full well it would be checked. Unfortunately, again for legal reasons, I cannot say all I would like on this matter. If I hadn't volunteered the term and put it in my affidavit, the Cunneen Inquiry would have been none the wiser, but like I said, I was determined to put everything on the table. Ultimately, with parts of my affidavit redacted, the Cunneen Inquiry took another person's word over mine.

•

Earlier I said not everyone was playing by the same rules. I had handed everything over, even material I knew would be to my detriment. I knew the police force was required to do the same.

I have to live with the findings of the Cunneen Inquiry – and as devastating as they are to me and to Penny, I know the truth of my actions. The reason I fought so hard was because that was the only way I thought I could protect those who had been abused, and help in the prosecution of abusers and anyone who in any way enabled that abuse to occur.

When Anthea Halpin called me in mid-December 2010 saying she felt intimidated by police demands to take her statement in relation to her sexual abuse by her uncle, Denis McAlinden, and her concern at the failure of the Church to notify police of that abuse, I had been oblivious to other events. In cross-examination it was put to one of the investigating officers that at a meeting with Joanne McCarthy and Andrew Morrison SC in late 2010, he had described Anthea as 'aggressive and difficult to deal with'.

The officer denied having made the comment. In any case, it wasn't my experience with Anthea. She was cooperative, keen to provide a statement and see the case progress.

Mark Cohen was keen to explore the evidence further, but Patrick Saidi teamed up with the officer's lawyer in a bid to stop Mark's questioning. Martin Rush, representing Joanne McCarthy, argued Mark be allowed to continue. I too sensed something was being withheld. After Commissioner Cunneen said she didn't see any relevance in Mark's approach, I feared Mark's questioning would be stopped. Barrister Warwick Hunt, another counsel assisting the Cunneen Inquiry, suggested a non-publication order on that passage of evidence. At this point Rush handed Hunt a document. It caused Hunt to step back. He told Commissioner Cunneen it was something he 'hadn't seen before and hadn't been served or provided by the NSW Police Force to those assisting you'.

Commissioner Cunneen called a hasty adjournment to convene a meeting behind closed doors.

Murmuring continued outside as everyone milled about wondering what was going on. It seemed serious. I am unable to detail exactly what happened for legal reasons, but it backed up what Anthea had previously told me. She was upset at how she was treated and didn't think the police did the right thing by her. I have to agree.

The Cunneen Inquiry redacted twenty-two pages of transcript around this concern. With police having withheld a document, I wondered if there were other documents that weren't produced. Some police must have been relieved when the Cunneen Inquiry redacted the transcript surrounding this unsavoury incident. I cannot express enough my frustration at not being able to legally say more about this issue.

CHAPTER 29

OPERATION PROTEA

ABC-TV's Suzie Smith ran another story about the Catholic Church's Professional Standards Resource Group (PSRG) in June 2013. It centred on internal police papers that disclosed that a NSW detective sat on a Church board deliberating child sexual abuse as part of her duties. At the completion of each meeting, she shredded documents. Former head of the DPP Nicholas Cowdery, likened it to destroying evidence.

Suzie's story caused quite a stir, with police announcing the Cunneen Inquiry would consider the issue. While the police minister called the police commissioner for an urgent briefing, Mark Cohen and I, after our failed attempt to have the matter examined back in April 2013, prepared another submission. Blind reporting was finally going to be examined.

Everything looked promising when the Inquiry asked for my notes concerning Denis McAlinden's blind reports. Julia Lonergan, after acknowledging the police department's referral, the *Lateline* program and our submission, quashed the idea, declaring there was presently no evidence the PSRG ever dealt with matters involving Denis McAlinden or James Fletcher. Considering the notes I had provided, I was left perplexed. The next day the minister announced that blind reporting would be referred to the Police Integrity Commission (PIC) instead. Mark was assured all applicable documents would be forwarded.

Following the Cunneen Inquiry, I spoke at various child abuse forums, attended advocacy fundraisers and supported survivors at the Child Abuse Royal Commission. I had almost given up on blind reporting ever being examined when, in October 2014, a month before my discharge from the NSW Police Force, a newspaper article announced that the PIC's Operation Protea, tasked with investigating blind reporting, was holding its hearing the next week. Anyone with information was asked to contact the PIC. I couldn't understand why they hadn't yet contacted me. I sent an email to the address listed in the newspaper with an updated submission. Fifteen minutes later, my phone rang.

My submission and its references troubled Detective Kim Modra. Explaining it was essentially the same submission I provided a year earlier, I told him, 'It would have been forwarded by the Cunneen Inquiry with the other documents.'

I could hear him thinking before he asked, 'Could you email us another copy of your original submission?'

Now I was troubled. 'You already have it, don't you?'

They probably did, he assured me. 'It would just save us having to look. And can you also send the other documents?'

I sent my original submission explaining I no longer had the other documents. With Protea's public hearing only days away, Detective Modra called back before handing the phone to solicitor Ben Broyd. Ben was more concerned about the 'other documents'. I told him: 'They were all supposed to be forwarded to you by the Cunneen Inquiry.'

Ben asked about the correspondence between Police Commissioner Ryan and Cardinal Clancy. Then there were questions about the 1997 draft MOU between police and the Catholic Church, the involvement of Brian Lucas, and issues with Towards Healing and the MOU conflicting with the law. Without saying they didn't have the documents, it seemed obvious to me Ben knew nothing about them. What had happened to them? I knew they weren't the sort of thing that gets lost down the back of a fridge. I made some calls, and the documents turned up at the eleventh hour.

I wasn't asked to be a witness, though I did attend the PIC hearings. Patrick Saidi represented police and asked how the PIC obtained the missing documents. I wondered how he knew they had been missing.

I wasn't surprised when the hearing revealed that Denis McAlinden was part of the PSRG process. I also saw James Fletcher's name on a document. Both priests had been part of the Cunneen Inquiry's terms of reference. Here was the proof linking both to blind reporting.

The PIC released its report in June 2015. It confirmed NSW Police ignored repeated legal warnings against establishing an informal arrangement between itself and the Catholic Church. PIC Commissioner Bruce James QC concluded that blind reporting meant many complaints were never investigated. It was the same assessment I made when I first learned of the process.

Condemnation came from many quarters. Deputy Ombudsman Steve Kinmond pointed out there could be 'over a thousand [blind] reports on the wrong side of the law'.

Survivors Network of those Abused by Priests (SNAP) spokesperson Nicky Davis, a survivor herself, was outraged, demanding an explanation and calling for NSW Police to apologise to survivors. Nicholas Cowdery went further: 'it was a conspiracy to thwart the criminal justice process, and the police force was a party to it'.

Notwithstanding the condemnation, the PIC didn't demand changes, but concluded that the police officers were 'well intentioned'.

Despite continuing to conflict with the law, there was no resolve to stop blind reporting, simply a recommendation for review. Police deflected attention by highlighting the 'well intentioned' officers. Blind reporting continued.

•

I sat in on a Child Abuse Royal Commission roundtable on blind reporting in April 2016. The next day the ABC reported a huge increase in blind reporting to NSW Police since the Child Abuse Royal Commission had started. David Shoebridge revealed that NSW Police processed 1476 blind reports in eight years. Why the rush? Some blind reports contained multiple victims. Considering the seven reports I found on Denis McAlinden contained fifteen victims, it is conceivable that the total surpassed three thousand. Recorded as 'intelligence only', the vast majority were never investigated or recorded as a crime. Government bodies and the public, therefore, had no idea of the true scale of child sexual abuse within the Catholic Church.

Denise Laverie told the ABC that the Catholic Church hadn't forwarded her 1995 statement to police. Denise and I had already confirmed a 2009 blind report was based on her statement to the Church fourteen years earlier. She had never told anyone she didn't want police involved, yet there it was, tucked away in Church archives until after McAlinden's death. The Church never disclosed when it first took the report. NSW

Police blindly accepted that Denise didn't want them involved. There was no investigation and, of course, no questions were asked. Denise told the ABC she felt let down: 'It was the Church protecting their own as far as I'm concerned.'

Another abuse survivor told the ABC that when he reported his abuse to the Catholic Church in 2011, Church authorities told him it would be passed on to police. Instead, the Church blind reported his allegation, again withholding the survivor's name. That's how it worked – with no name, there could be no investigation. The survivor rhetorically asked, 'What's the point of telling the police about an allegation without giving them the full information so that they can investigate? Blind reporting, I think, should be against the law.'

Police prosecutor Sergeant Allan Treadwell and others had already pointed out that blind reporting was incongruent with the law, but despite this, NSW Police refused to abandon the process. It was left to Francis Sullivan of the Catholic Church's Truth, Justice and Healing Council in April 2016 to concede, 'It's absolutely regrettable if people were under the impression that their name was going to be given to the police and it wasn't ... The practice now is that regardless of individual preferences, the name of the perpetrators and the names of victims are given to the police.'

If the argument for blind reporting was that it avoided a breach of confidence, how did this argument suddenly disappear? The Church didn't say if the 1476 victim names previously withheld would now be passed on to police, or if NSW Police would alter all past blind-reported intelligence to be recorded as crimes.

In any case, at least as far as the Church was concerned, blind reporting was over, but at what cost? I was left pondering if the Church had avoided prosecution for concealing child sexual abuse by notifying police through blind reporting. In other words, because Denise's complaint was technically reported, did it let senior clergy who knew about her abuse off the hook? I'm not sure, but if it did, how many times, in relation to how many victims did this occur?

Established on the offending institution's own terms, blind reporting ensured decades of child sexual abuse went under the statistical radar. If 1476 rapes were reported in eight years at public schools, universities or any other institution, there would have been a public outcry. With the Catholic Church's crimes recorded as 'intelligence only', no one knew the extent of the abuse, with the exception of Church authorities, its perpetrators and their victims.

Considered advice, both internal and external, confirmed that blind reporting was incongruent with the law. Put simply, it was illegal. Bulldozing all opposition, NSW Police ignored this advice. The question is, why? It has been suggested that blind reporting was set up to record crimes that might otherwise not have been reported at all. I don't buy it. There was an obligation on everyone, the Catholic Church included, to report all knowledge of child sexual abuse. Circumventing the law to do what the law already required made no sense. Was investigating so many child abuse allegations too big a drain on police resources? Was acknowledging a problem that went undetected for so long too embarrassing? Or was it something else? I don't know, but what I do know is that many abuse survivors waited for police investigations that never came. It remains to be seen if civil courts will hold anyone liable.

CHAPTER 30

A QUIET DEATH

When I was discharged from the NSW Police Force soon after Operation Protea concluded, my office belongings arrived in a cardboard box. Photos, power cords, books, computer discs – you name it – all thrown together in confusion. Unpacking with Penny and our daughter, I found a presentation box crushed under a weighty conglomeration of odds and ends. My National Police Service Medal was thus presented.

Months later, a surprise retirement function was organised by Penny and some friends – with only one serving officer turning up in a room full of former colleagues.

The absence of serving police was more than compensated for by a collage of people I had helped over my career. I particularly choked up hugging Kelly Parker; in 1999, I investigated the murder of her five-year-old daughter. Chrissie and Anthony Foster sat with Lou and Pam Pirona, all parents who had lost children to the evil of clergy child sexual abuse. Daniel Feenan and others also attended. Their presence meant a lot.

•

Later in 2015, I contacted Glen Walsh, the good priest. We had thought it best not to speak until after the Cunneen Inquiry. I travelled to see him on the Central Coast, and he broke into tears as he hugged me. Gone was the resilient man I had met in 2004, now a shadow of his former self. The past decade had really knocked him about, both mentally and physically.

We had lunch at a restaurant overlooking the beach, but God's wonders no longer interested him. I took Glen back to his home where he was more at ease. If I thought I'd had a rough time, Glen had endured worse. After going behind the Bishop's back to bring an abuse survivor to me, the Church sent Glen to Coventry. Glen said a senior clergyman had told him, 'Fuck off out of my Diocese and don't come back.'

Glen told me he had been ill and had nursing staff by his side when cross-examined by the Cunneen Inquiry away from the public. He said the Inquiry and Church lawyers exacted a heavy toll. Glen was most upset by attacks he said were aimed at the two of us. Like Daniel Feenan, he felt the whole process was one-sided.

After this ordeal Glen remained cut off. A few priests cared, but most never phoned, let alone visited, with others being downright cruel. It reminded me of the ostracism meted out to Maurie Crocker all those years ago in Wollongong.

As I drove home, Glen's image haunted me: a beaten man, dejected and rejected by the Church he loved. I wanted to do something, but what? Who was there to complain to? In desperation I did something that surprised even me: I wrote to the Pope. Yes, that's right, the pontiff himself. My letter probably never got to the Pope, just one of his minders, but I wanted someone, anyone, to know the plight of this good priest. I also wanted them to know someone outside the Church knew what was happening. The Vatican delegated

Bishop Bill Wright from the Maitland–Newcastle Diocese to address my concerns. He explained Glen had mental health issues he couldn't discuss. I already knew – Glen had told me. What caused those issues is what I wanted to talk about: the ostracism, the hurt and the unchristian behaviour inflicted by fellow clergy. Wright gave me a fair hearing and respected my request that Glen not be told of my letter.

In February 2017, Bishop Wright welcomed Glen back to the Diocese. He acknowledged the ill feeling when Glen broke ranks to assist with my investigation of James Fletcher, telling fellow clergy: 'he [Glen] should be welcomed. Those who disagreed with his actions in the past will, I hope, be able to acknowledge that Glen did what he believed to be right then, and what we know to be right now. He did it at considerable cost to himself, and that needs to be respected.'

Glen was thrilled by his return to the fold, but remained apprehensive. When contacted by detectives attached to Strike Force Lantle to give evidence concerning Archbishop Wilson, Glen again felt vulnerable, telling me we shouldn't talk until it was over. I just hoped the Church and police would give Glen the support he needed.

•

When Denise visited Anthea in 2016 they suggested we catch up. It was a gathering the NSW Police and the Cunneen Inquiry would not have anticipated. Strike Force Lantle had charged Adelaide's Archbishop, Philip Wilson, with concealing child sexual abuse the previous year, based on Peter Creigh's allegation that he told Philip Wilson in 1976 that he had been sexually abused by priest James Fletcher. The charge was not connected to Lantle's original investigation concerning Wilson's involvement surrounding the crimes of Denis McAlinden. Over lunch the sisters told me they no longer expected anyone to be charged with concealing McAlinden's crimes. Neither had heard from police in years. They just assumed their complaints, like those to the Church, had died a quiet death. Six years after Lantle began, I agreed they were unlikely to be resurrected now. Anthea and Denise were told nothing, nor were the media or the public informed. A quiet death was an apt description.

Denise then dropped a bombshell. 'After the way they treated us and losing my statement, I'm not surprised it went nowhere.'

Confused, I asked, 'Lost your statement? What do you mean lost your statement?'

'That's what I wanted to tell you. The police lost the statement you took from me.'

'You're kidding. Are you sure?'

I was stunned. Why hadn't the Cunneen Inquiry explored this? I thought about my report, the one that couldn't be found, with excerpts from Denise's statement. It too had disappeared. Was the loss of both just coincidence?

There was no mention of this in any police statement to the Cunneen Inquiry. Not only did the investigating officer not mention it, not a single police officer said a word. Something like this had to be known to the entire Strike Force Lantle team.

'If it was lost,' I asked, 'why didn't someone call me?'

Denise had no explanation. As was standard practice, I had saved the electronic version. It was only a matter of reprinting and having Denise sign it again. I even attached a copy to my Cunneen Inquiry affidavit. It was that simple. There was no need to put Denise though any of this.

If Denise's statement had been innocently misplaced or lost, why not come out and say that? Sure it might have been embarrassing, but at least it would have been forthright and honest.

Denise had known all about her sister's torment, Anthea's unsympathetic dealings with Lantle and her tears to me over the phone. She also knew about Anthea's complaints about how she felt during the process. Neither were shrinking violets. Being retired nurses, they had been through the school of hard knocks, raised families and seen a fair bit of life. They knew how the world worked. Being survivors of shocking childhood abuse, they just wanted to see justice and be treated compassionately. It wasn't a lot to ask.

There was a lot to take in and I sat trying to figure everything out and understand why I hadn't learned of any of this until now. Anthea then spoke, supporting her sister by telling me that she too was told by police that Denise's statement was lost.

'When did they tell you that?'

'About October 2010.'

That didn't make sense as this was around the same time my office was searched for the Church brief, so I believed Anthea must have been mistaken about the date she was told of the lost statement. I explained how Denise's statement had been safely locked in my office safe until 2 December 2010 when I was told to surrender it, so I reasoned Anthea couldn't have been told before then. Put simply, Lantle couldn't say they had lost what they didn't have? Anthea wouldn't budge on her memory of the date. She was certain. She then told me she could prove it. On 9 November 2010, a month before she had phoned me in tears, she said she had sent an email to five senior police complaining of the way she was being treated by the strike force. She had double checked the date of the email before coming to see me. Anthea said the purpose of her email was to complain about her treatment by Lantle, believing their approach to her was such that a complainant would walk away and not press for investigations to continue. I remembered recording a similar comment in Barbara's statement, when she too walked away from the Church investigation back in the 1990s.

As Anthea continued, she told me she also asked police why there appeared to be such little interest in pursuing her complaint and why it appeared no one wanted to upset the Catholic Church. All that was important, but I wanted to go back to her being told in October 2010 that Denise's statement was lost.

Anthea confirmed to me that she had raised being informed of the lost statement in her November email, saying she was told by a detective attached to Strike Force Lantle they had lost Denise's statement. She also vented about other issues. So, not only was Denise told her statement was lost, but Anthea was also told, even before I had given the statement to Lantle. I had read the affidavits of all senior police who gave evidence at the Cunneen Inquiry, including those to whom Anthea had sent her email. Not one said a word about any of this, nor, to my knowledge was the failure of losing Denise's statement examined by the Inquiry.

That day, I also learned that six months after the initial call, Lantle rang Denise one last time. Passed around like a football, it was another call from yet another detective. After police had lost her statement, Denise had walked away in disgust. Now her statement miraculously turned up. Would she finish it? By this time Denise had well and truly had enough. As far as she was concerned, it was too late. She didn't complete her statement and never heard from Lantle again.

Was Denise's relocated statement sent to the DPP with what was described in evidence at the Cunneen Inquiry as Lantle's 'amazing' brief? Denise doesn't know, nor is she aware if Lantle disclosed to the DPP the fact that she walked away. All this might be what was alluded to when an officer told the Cunneen Inquiry, 'There may be a failure down the track, but it certainly has to do with the quality of what the police have had to work with, not the way in which they have worked with it.'

This sounds like blaming the victims. My lawyers and I weren't permitted to hear Anthea and Denise give evidence. It meant we couldn't hear of Anthea's complaint, or learn about Denise's lost statement. It turned out there was good reason. Anthea and Denise told me they never got in a witness box, even in closed court. Instead they were privately interviewed by Margaret Cunneen and Julia Lonergan. Denise said Commissioner Cunneen was most concerned about Denise's belief that the Church intended to take her complaint to police, asking if I had put those words in her mouth. Denise said she was firm, telling Cunneen the words were hers.

•

In 2012, Lantle forwarded its McAlinden brief to the DPP. I doubt Helen Keever's incomplete and unsigned statement was included. Denise's statement wasn't finished and Anthea's wasn't signed. No prosecution eventuated. As Anthea said, it *'died a quiet death'*.

•

Before commencing, the Cunneen Inquiry found something Lantle had missed. Hidden in the Maitland–Newcastle Diocese was yet another time bomb, a 2010 letter from Peter Creigh to Bishop Malone. It was the same year senior police praised Malone for his assistance, yet it would seem Malone told them nothing about this damning letter. When the letter surfaced in 2013, James Fletcher had been dead seven years. Nothing could be done on that account, however the letter said more. It revealed that in 1976, Peter allegedly told Father Philip Wilson he had been sexually assaulted by Fletcher.

As the Child Abuse Royal Commission prepared to examine the Catholic Church, the letter somehow ended up in the hands of the Cunneen Inquiry. The crimes against Peter Creigh and their alleged concealment happened in Maitland, however the Inquiry didn't send the investigation to the Maitland Command, instead handing it to Newcastle's Strike Force Lantle. It seems this is when the Cunneen Inquiry expanded its TOR to include Fletcher. As Lantle began a new investigation, few noticed the McAlinden investigation slip from view.

Presiding over Wilson's hearing, Magistrate Robert Stone would later say the investigation was referred to investigators attached to the Special Commission. It was an understandable enough mistake. However, Strike Force Lantle wasn't attached to the Cunneen Inquiry; Lantle's conduct was supposed to be examined by the Inquiry. Lantle, it seemed, had the Inquiry's confidence before hearings even began.

It wasn't long before I heard about Lantle's latest investigation. In 2016, a year before Glen Walsh was welcomed back into the Maitland–Newcastle Diocese, he called me to say he was a witness and so we couldn't again talk until after he had given evidence. Everything I had been saying in 2010, the significance of Fletcher's abuse survivor Adam, Adam's sister Holly, Holly's husband and their extended family's interactions with the Church, now became important to Lantle, and an officer asked them for statements.

Although I had left the Police Force two years earlier, in 2016 I fielded fresh calls from witnesses complaining about Lantle. Some initially refused to provide statements. Others told me they complained to the Crown Prosecutor about the conduct of one of Lantle's investigators. Lantle's staff appeared to have learned little.

Around the same time, Pat Feenan told police that their statements should have been obtained years before, when first suggested by me. Although they separated, Pat and John Feenan remained good friends and never divorced. Sadly, John died in late 2015. Pat pointed out to police that had they commenced the investigation years earlier, John's knowledge could have assisted.

Pat also told them she was aware of Peter Creigh following Peter approaching me after the Newcastle Forum in 2012. Although I had forgotten his surname, Pat had discovered Peter's identity through the Hunter grapevine. She often says the Hunter only has two degrees of separation, and she's probably right. Had Lantle been proactive in touting for survivors, Peter Creigh could have been spoken to much earlier.

When Wilson was charged in 2015 (well before he was acquitted), I offered the DPP a statement. Believing Peter Creigh had taken my advice in speaking with police, I mentioned our 2012 conversation. The DPP declined my offer.

•

In 2018, two women sat in the back of a Newcastle Court glaring at Adelaide's Archbishop. Unlike Peter Creigh, who had been a teenager when he told Wilson of his abuse, Anthea and Denise had been adults. In any case, Wilson never told police about any of them. The court might not have allowed Anthea and Denise's 'tendency and coincidence evidence', but no attempt was even made to introduce it, so we'll never know.

Magistrate Robert Stone convicted Wilson, and a successful appeal was lodged by Wilson's barrister, Stephen Odgers SC against his conviction. One argument Odgers used was that Peter Creigh never told Wilson that Fletcher used physical force amounting to an assault. For a charge of concealing a serious offence to succeed in New South Wales, the crime being concealed must carry a penalty of five years gaol or more. An indecent act did not meet that standard, whereas an indecent *assault* did. In the 1970s, a child directed to perform a sex act on an adult didn't necessarily constitute an assault. Odgers put it this way: 'If the adult inserts his penis into the child, that clearly is a battery. If the adult says to the child, "I want you to put your mouth over my penis," that's not.'

Odgers didn't challenge Peter Creigh, telling Wilson he had been sexually abused by Fletcher. His argument, in addition to saying the original crime did not amount to an assault, was his client simply didn't remember Peter Creigh telling him anything of this nature.

It might seem pedantic to us outside the legal profession, but at law it was a legitimate issue and would prove a significant failing in the police brief.

Unfortunately, the fact that Peter Creigh approached me in 2012 was not disclosed to the court. This was despite the DPP having my email that stated, 'I am the first police officer the victim in the current case approached with his complaint of abuse by Fletcher and reporting of that abuse.'

When Peter approached me in 2012, I was still a police officer and he wouldn't have known I was absent on leave. I am not suggesting this information would have altered the outcome, but my point is that the court should have been told. It led Judge Ellis to say Peter Creigh made no attempt to approach anyone outside his family.

Sitting in the appeal court, I picked up on other issues. Odgers said Wilson gave evidence of never having received a direct complaint. Judge Ellis highlighted, 'He [Wilson] says that no one ever complained to him, but I think it might be fair to say that he was saying no one ever complain[ed] to him outside of [the] confessional.'

Barbara's statement revealed she disclosed her childhood sexual abuse to Wilson in 1982–83. Mike Stanwell's statement said in 1986 Wilson spoke to a Merriwa mother about Denis McAlinden's crimes. In 1995, Wilson not only listened to Denise's and Anthea's complaints, but typed their statements. I provided all these documents and more to Lantle and the Cunneen Inquiry. Should the court have been told?

Odgers also asserted that Wilson 'was not a person in 2004 who was motivated to keep these kinds of allegations quiet'.

The court found that Wilson didn't remember Peter Creigh complaining in 1976. Odgers emphasised Wilson's positive history in dealing with abuse allegations. Judge Ellis was told that Wilson's approach was not to believe an allegation unless an offender admitted his crimes or a legal process had occurred; 'He would sit on the fence. He would neither positively believe, nor would he disbelieve it.'

When Barbara told Wilson of her sexual abuse, she didn't expect Wilson to approach police. That said, she told me she knew Wilson *believed* her. After speaking to the mother of the abused child in Merriwa, Mike Stanwell was told, 'something has definably gone on'.

Should the court have been told all this when deciding if Wilson always 'sat on the fence'?

Judge Ellis overturned Wilson's conviction, with the DPP saying it had no grounds to appeal. All this material I have mentioned might not have changed the result, but we will never know. I do know that Peter Creigh and others were left devastated. Senior clergy's ailing memories were something the country became used to during the Child Abuse Royal Commission. In the court of public opinion Wilson's failing memory was met with understandable scepticism, though as Judge Ellis noted, the period of time involved decades.

Someone who didn't see Wilson acquitted was Father Glen Walsh. Weeks before he was due to give evidence, I was devastated to hear that Glen had reportedly taken his own life. When we last spoke, Glen was scared, but determined to see it through. He believed in the truth and told me God would guide him. Maybe so, but that didn't ease Glen's fears. I could hear his apprehension.

As I am completing the edit to this book in April 2019, the ABC-TV's *7.30 Report* disclosed that in the lead up to Wilson's trial, Peter Creigh told police of threats and intimidation from persons who didn't want him to give evidence. ABC-TV journalist, Ben Millington, raised the question about whether Glen Walsh might have received similar intimidation. Jeff Little told him, 'He [Glen Walsh] certainly told me he was petrified about giving evidence against senior members of his Church and, regrettably, the evidence that he could have given, actually went with him to his passing.'

Glen had been appalled by clergy abuse and revolted by those who concealed it. He once told me younger priests wanted to see change, but older hands continued to rule his Church with an iron fist. I can still hear Glen's gentle voice. He didn't just talk about what was right, he did what was right, despite the cost. After this sad episode, Glen's brother, John, and sister, Trish, vowed never to walk into a Catholic Church again. The family held a private funeral conducted by one of the few priests who remained Glen's friend. Like Maurie Crocker, Glen was the sort of priest to whom the Church should build monuments.

EPILOGUE

I initially wrote this story jumping from one topic to another in a disorganised jumble as I attempted to deal with what happened. As time went on, I re-worded, merged, added and subtracted what I legally couldn't say, trying to bring it all together in some semblance of chronology. I hope it has worked.

This last chapter is difficult. There is so much more I could have said. I hope my story doesn't disparage or cast the whole NSW Police Force in a negative light. That was not my intention. It was a job I loved and, if given the chance, would do it all again. I still have a sibling and other family serving as police, and regularly catch up with past colleagues. I have shared parts of my story with many who just nod their heads. Like me, they joined young and naive, learning as they went that not everything is perfect.

Police, as in any profession, come from all walks of life. The vast majority are good people who strive to do the best they can, often under very trying circumstances.

Over my thirty-six–year career, I enjoyed the camaraderie and mateship of a close-knit profession. Exposed to so much of the ugly side, many police adopt a *Fort Apache* mentality, us against them, building stronger and sometimes unethical bonds between those inside. There will always be those who abuse trust and power, as much as there will be those who will try to hold them to account. It is a struggle that has been going on since time immemorial, and will no doubt continue. I am now happy to pass on my baton.

I lost some police friends as I embarked along this final journey. Looking back, in all reality, they were probably friends I knew at work and we would have drifted apart regardless. Many disliked me for holding police to account, particularly when I stood up and spoke out about clergy abuse. Many lent quiet support. Others I can only describe as cowards who failed to stand up and chose to hide in the safety of the herd. The vast majority of police were neutral, watching from the sidelines. Others expressed neither support nor opposition, preferring to keep their heads down. It's not something unique to police. I'm sure most people have experienced similar in a vast array of fields. Seeing what's wrong, some are disinclined to become involved unless they are personally impacted, and even then, they would prefer to look the other way. Why get involved and expose yourself to hardship and grief if you don't have to? It's human nature, and I don't judge them harshly. During my career I probably did the same. There were times I could have made a stronger stance for one thing or another, injustice or wrongdoing. In retrospect, had I stood up then, I probably wouldn't have been around when the clergy abuse scandal erupted. I had no vested interest, I just saw what was happening and wasn't prepared to be one of those who did nothing.

•

Some have asked if I would have taken a stand had I not been at the end of my career. I have thought about that, a lot. I still had seven years to go until my planned retirement at sixty. The answer is, I don't know. I would like to say I would have, but I really don't know. I was certainly at the end of a long career, having accumulated a lot of experience, both positive and negative. All were factors contributing to my stance.

Reflecting on what brought about a Child Abuse Royal Commission, there were many contributors. I reject people saying my standing up was the key component; it wasn't. Suzie Smith was closer to the mark in saying I was the tipping point. Many things contributed to my stance, particularly getting to know survivors and their families. The books written by Chrissie Foster (with Paul Kennedy) and Pat Feenan had a strong influence. When I said earlier that books can be powerful, I meant it. My reputation led Joanne McCarthy to approach me, resulting in my speaking to Barbara, Anthea, Denise and school principal Mike Stanwell, among others. Had one ingredient been missing, one planet not aligned, a prime minister not been compassionate enough to act, the Child Abuse Royal Commission might not have happened. Above all, I had the support of my family. Alongside myself, Penny had to bear the brunt of reprisals, standing by me as I carried my cross. It wasn't easy.

That was just my part, and many others worked towards the same goal. Advocacy groups and individual survivors stood up and the media carried their voice. When governments and law enforcement failed, journalists and editors took the ball up in a tireless pursuit of the truth. We owe them.

Peter Cullen's, Suzie Smith's, Joanne McCarthy's and other journalists' ongoing pursuit of clergy abuse concealment was essential when politicians and police looked the other way.

Brian Lucas never mentioned government or police when he warned, 'What the media will search for is the cover-up, or the failure of the Church to act appropriately.'

Lucas acknowledged the media was the Church's greatest fear because it could expose the whole sordid mess. The Church could influence the media though sympathetic commentators, but it could never hope to control it.

Again I would like to make the point, when I criticised police failure to investigate those crimes, some tried to muddy the water by saying I was critical of all police, including those who were arresting priests. Nothing could be further from the truth, but it suited an agenda of turning police and public thinking against me. The question still looms large as to why law enforcement across the nation didn't investigate the concealment of clergy abuse when the crime seemed so obvious to most.

●

I am not the first police officer to have been put through the wringer. After I spoke out, Constable Lucie Litchfield's testimony supported two men charged with assault. Lucie didn't know the men, but her evidence supported their version of events over her workmates, with the magistrate describing her evidence as 'cogent and compelling'.

I don't know Lucie or any of those involved, I just read her story, but, like most, I asked myself what she had to gain. The assault charges against the two men were eventually dropped, costing NSW taxpayers half a million dollars in damages. An internal police investigation found no wrongdoing. No surprises there. Following ongoing ostracism, Lucie resigned. She too had broken rank to do what she believed was right.

Her male colleagues maintained their Commander's confidence with one promoted and the other starting a detective career. The police force still has a long way to go.

•

Invited to speak at the launch of *Unholy Trinity*, I initially had no idea who former Victorian Detective Denis Ryan was, or what his book was about. You can imagine my surprise when, reading the manuscript, I came across not only the term but a chapter titled 'The Catholic Mafia'.

In 1970s Mildura, Denis investigated Catholic priest Monsignor John Day for child sexual abuse. Fearing senior police would stop his investigation, Denis took statements from survivors in secret. When I got to page 148, I had to walk outside for some air. Telling his superintendent what he had been investigating, Denis was directed to hand over all his statements and was removed from the investigation. Day was never brought to justice and Denis was forced out of the police force. Avoiding duplication wasn't a concern when Denis gave evidence to the Child Abuse Royal Commission.

Penny and I got to know Denis when we visited his cherished city of Mildura. Now well in his eighties, Denis remains nature's gentleman, exuding integrity and an inspiration to many. It took forty years for Denis to be vindicated.

•

Melbourne. Ballarat. Canberra. Sydney. Brisbane. Newcastle. Wherever the Child Abuse Royal Commission sat, Penny and I followed. We listened to evidence and supported survivors. During hearings in Rome, Penny and I tied ribbons to the windows of Domus Australia, a multi-million dollar residence purchased by Cardinal Pell on behalf of his Church. The ribbon idea started in the abuse epicentre of Ballarat and spread worldwide as a symbol of support for survivors and victims of childhood sexual abuse. Following the national apology to abuse survivors in Canberra, this symbolism was formalised with ribbons being tied to a bronze tree artwork outside parliament.

•

For years we listened to evidence and supported survivors at the Child Abuse Royal Commission. We had teamed up with Chrissie and Anthony Foster, joining Ian and Joan Isaacs, our close-knit group, not just at hearings, but socially as well. We had all become advocates and friends. I am told reporters at the hearings began referring to us as 'the three couples'.

In 2017, Penny and I spent a wonderful day with Chrissie and Anthony in Melbourne, but then, just a few days later, we received a devastating call. Anthony had collapsed and died. A torrent of tears. We had lost a wonderful friend, and survivors had lost an amazing advocate. I wasn't surprised when Victorian Premier Daniel Andrews honoured Anthony with a state funeral.

Flying back to Melbourne I felt numb. At Anthony's funeral, Penny and I saw people we had come to know from all over the country. It was then I realised we had unknowingly become part of something bigger, a community born of the Royal Commission, all supporting one another.

We spent the next morning with Chrissie at her home watching her immerse herself in grandchildren and family.

Saying 'Anthony and Chrissie' was just normal, that's how it was, their names just went together like Torvill and Dean,

Napoleon and Josephine. They were a team. It took time to get used to saying 'Chrissie' alone. But Anthony had taught his family to be strong. It wasn't long before Chrissie was back writing articles, doing television and radio interviews, and travelling to support others.

Joan, Ian, Penny and I all join Chrissie in Melbourne once a year, a get-together we intend to continue. A toast to Anthony and 'the three couples'.

•

I came from a long line of Catholics. My mum still has her mother's and grandmother's photos hanging at home, adorned with rosary beads and other religious paraphernalia. I was raised part Anglican, part Catholic, with a bit of Church of Christ thrown in, and then I married in the Uniting Church – so, you could probably say I was a Christian crossbreed. Penny and I weren't regular churchgoers, but we chose to send our kids to Catholic schools and attend Easter, Christmas and other services in the Catholic Church. What I'm saying is, I'm not anti-Catholic, and never have been.

Our youngest granddaughter arrived unexpectedly while Penny and I sat in the Cunneen Inquiry. Our son helped deliver her at his home before the ambulance arrived. I have a photo of me holding my granddaughter standing beside Father Brian Mascord, now Bishop of Wollongong. I have spoken to many priests and invited some to our home. While no longer Christian myself, I know that many are good men. We need more men like Maurie Crocker, Kevin Lee and Glen Walsh if the Church is to change, truly change.

When the Wood Royal Commission exposed police corruption, showing detectives using drugs, taking bribes and cavorting with prostitutes, I too hung my head, despite knowing I had done nothing wrong. Guilt by association. I can therefore empathise with the many good priests hiding their white collars. Many want to see their Church change.

That said, the Church is still being ruled by old men with iron fists, as Glen Walsh so poignantly put it. Like the police force and elsewhere, the internal struggle between good and bad within the Church will go on. The Catholic Church continues to resist change and for that reason we should never take our eyes off it, or any institution for that matter. Our children are too precious. The Church will need help to change, and much will have to come from outside, both offered and imposed.

•

Everything I said in my open letter to Premier O'Farrell, that the Church covered-up, silenced victims, hindered police investigations, alerted offenders, destroyed evidence and moved priests to protect the good name of the Church, was vindicated.

The Child Abuse Royal Commission made many recommendations. Some have been implemented while others remain under consideration, such as mandatory reporting of child sexual abuse, even when disclosed within the confessional, and a fair redress system for survivors of institutional child sexual abuse to replace the cruelty of processes like Towards Healing and the Melbourne Response. Politicians have a notoriously poor record when it comes to implementing all recommendations from such inquiries, or manipulating the spirit within those recommendations. The Catholic Church has already rejected implementing some important changes, so we need to ensure our governments don't do the same.

Even before the Child Abuse Royal Commission finished, change happened. Those who for so long had been doubted, ignored or brushed aside, were now believed. The scale of child sexual abuse and the extent of the cover-up shocked our nation to its core with the community pledging, *never again*.

Survivors are now listened to and believed. A change that didn't need political or institutional approval.

Because the Child Abuse Royal Commission could only examine institutional abuse, many felt left out. There can be no doubt the majority of child abuse occurs in the family home. One day politicians may become sufficiently alarmed for this to also be examined. Until then, I am confident there will be flow-on benefits from the Child Abuse Royal Commission in respect to legislative and other changes to help all. Awareness has increased significantly, along with belief and support.

As for my family, being protected or cared for under the *Protected Disclosures Act* or police policies amounted to nothing more than lip service, with written complaints resulting in little, if any action. I would even go so far as to suggest the inaction amounted to complicity. Little has changed since the days of Philip Arantz. While the public appreciate the role and risks taken by whistle-blowers, hidden behind supportive statements, governments and institutions continue to attack them.

Many police involved in Strike Force Lantle were lauded for their roles, given awards or promoted. Senior members of the Cunneen Inquiry were appointed Supreme Court judges.

Me, I'm still recovering while immersing myself in the life of our four beautiful granddaughters, with hopefully more to come.

•

The Church child sexual abuse scandal and its cover-up resulted in untold harm and cost the lives of John Pirona, Damien Jurd, Daniel Powell, Andrew Nash and hundreds of other children and adults. Along the way I lost friends such as John Feenan, Anthony Foster, Helen Keevers, Kevin Lee and Glen Walsh. To that can be added good people like Maurie Crocker, and the list goes on. The cost to our society is incalculable. My own health has suffered, and I lament the impact on my family. At times I have found myself asking, was it worth all the pain and torment?

Recently I walked my two youngest granddaughters to school. Aged seven and five, they are as beautiful as they are innocent. They held Pop's hand, one either side, as we crossed the road. Then it hit me. My beautiful girls are the same age as Anthony and Chrissie's daughters had been when they were abused. I kiss my girls goodbye knowing I can't be there every minute of every day. Our Child Abuse Royal Commission has changed Australian society forever, making the world a safer place for our kids. I have stopped asking myself if it was all worth it. Looking into my granddaughters' faces, I have my answer.

RESOURCE LIST

Lifeline Australia
13 11 14
24/7 crisis support and suicide prevention services
www.lifeline.org.au

Beyond Blue
1300 224 636
24/7 crisis support and suicide prevention services
www.beyondblue.org.au/get-support/national-help-lines-and-websites

Blue Knot Foundation
1300 657 380
9am–5pm Monday to Sunday AEST
www.blueknot.org.au

Bravehearts
1800 272 831
8.30am–4.30pm Monday to Friday AEST
bravehearts.org.au/who-we-are/contact-bravehearts

Care Leaver's Australasia Network
1800 008 774 / 0425 204 747
8.30am–4.30pm Monday to Friday AEST
www.clan.org.au

SAMSN
1800 472 676
9am–5pm Monday to Friday AEST
www.samsn.org.au/contact-us

ACKNOWLEDGEMENTS

I would like to thank the many abuse survivors and their families who have contributed to what I have written. Their voices and struggle to be heard is what inspired me. I would also like to thank the entire team at Hachette Australia, as compiling this book hasn't been easy. I would like to single out publisher Vanessa Radnidge, editor Brigid Mullane, and copy editor Claire de Medici who all worked tirelessly to make this book happen. A special thank you to author John Sutor Linton, who I met when he wrote a novel about a 2002 murder I had investigated. John provided this novice author with much advice and guidance along the path to this book. Finally, behind me has stood a great women. Penny has remained steadfastly by my side through every step of this journey. It has been a long one and her fortitude has been nothing short of remarkable, one of the many reasons I love her.

ABOUT THE AUTHOR

Former Detective Chief Inspector Peter Fox is a 36-year veteran of the NSW Police Force, during which time he investigated countless child sexual abuse cases in the Hunter Region of New South Wales. In November 2012, Peter Fox put his job on the line and went public with claims of systemic cover-up of institutional child abuse. His voice helped prompt the Royal Commission into Institutional Child Sexual Abuse. As a whistle-blower, Peter has made many enemies, and many have tried to discredit him. However, the victims and their families are strong in their support of the man who was always there for them, and who helped give them a voice. Peter continues to fight for victims and speak out against those who took advantage of their power to target and silence victims of abuse.

If you would like to find out more about
Hachette Australia, our authors, upcoming
events and new releases you can visit our
website or our social media channels:

hachette.com.au
HachetteAustralia
HachetteAus